The Open University

Faculty of
HEALTH
&
**SOCIAL
CARE**

K100

Understanding Health and
Social Care

Block 3

Care and
Communities

The Open University, Walton Hall, Milton Keynes MK7 6AA

First published 1998. Second edition 1999. Third edition 2003. Reprinted 2003, 2004 (with corrections). Fourth edition 2005.

Designed, edited and typeset by The Open University

Printed and bound in Malta by Gutenberg Press

ISBN 0 7492 1339 6

For information on Open University courses and study packs write to the Information Assistant, School of Health and Social Care, The Open University, Walton Hall, Milton Keynes MK7 6YY, phone 01908 653743, or visit www.open.ac.uk/shsw

4.1

K100 Course Team

Original production team

Andrew Northedge (Chair)
Jan Walmsley (Deputy Chair)
Margaret Allott
Tanya Hames (Course Secretary)
Joanna Bornat
Hilary Brown
Celia Davies
Roger Gomm
Sheila Peace
Martin Robb
Deborah Cooper (VQ Centre)

Jill Alger, Julie Fletcher (Editors); Janis Gilbert (Graphic Artist); Hannah Brunt, Rob Williams (Designers); Paul Smith (Librarian); Deborah Bywater (Project Control Assistant); Ann Carter (Print Buying Controller); Pam Berry (Text Processing Services); Mike Levers (Photographer); Vic Lockwood, Alison Tucker, Kathy Wilson (BBC Producers); Maggie Guillon (Cartoonist)

Staff tutors

Lindsay Brigham
Anne Fletcher
Carole Ulanowsky

External assessor

Professor Lesley Doyal, University of Bristol.

This is the K100 core course team. Many other people also contributed to making the course and their names are given in the Introduction and Study Guide.

Revision team

Andrew Northedge (Chair)
Corinne Pennifold
Christine Wild (Course Team Assistant)
James Blewett
Joanna Bornat
Hilary Brown
Sue Cusworth
Celia Davies
Marion Dunlop
Pam Foley
Tom Heller
Vijay Patel
Sheila Peace
Lucy Rai
Marion Reichart
Angela Russell
Geraldine Lee-Treweek
Danielle Turney
Jan Walmsley
Jo Warner

Hannah Brunt (Designer), Deborah Bywater (Project Control), Maggie Guillon (Cartoonist), Sara Hack (Graphic Artist), Lucy Hendy (Compositor), Julie Fletcher, Denise Lulham (Editors)

Critical readers

Fiona Harkes, Sylvia Caveney, Gillian Thompson, Katy Sainsbury, Eunice Lumsden, Lynne Fisher, Margaret Brown, Paula Faller, Kate Stilliard

External reviewers

Professor Gordon Grant, University of Sheffield; Mary McColgan, University of Ulster; Nigel Porter, University of Portsmouth

External assessor

Professor Gordon Grant, University of Sheffield

Contents

Study skills by Andrew Northedge

Introduction

The main focus of Block 2 was on the ways in which care is provided within people's homes, on the one hand, and in residential and institutional settings on the other. However, as far back as Unit 3, we noted the increasing emphasis within health and social care on the local community as a desirable setting for care services. As we saw there, 'community care' is often a shorthand for informal care provided within people's homes. However, providing services 'in the community' or 'working in the community' for health and social care often means much more than this. In Block 3, we examine what it means for services to be community-based. Unit 10 *Accessing Community Services* explores the kinds of health and care services that are to be found in local communities, and asks how accessible they are to the range of people they are designed to help. Unit 11 *Communities, Diversity and Care* discusses what communities mean to different groups of people and how communities respond to the health and social needs of differing groups within society. Unit 12 *Working with Communities* looks at how communities as a whole can improve health. Finally, Unit 13 *Finding Out about Services in the Community* – the skills unit for this block – gives you the chance to investigate the range of health and social care services available in your own local community, and to develop skills in using sources of information.

Unit 10
Accessing Community Services

Prepared for the course team by Jan Walmsley and Tom Heller,
updated by the authors with advice from Geraldine Lee-Treweek

While you are working on Unit 10, you will need:

- Course Reader
- Offprints Book
- *The Good Study Guide*
- Block 2, Unit 6
- Wallchart
- Care Systems and Structures

Contents

Introduction

In this first unit of Block 3 we explore questions of access to community services. To make what might be quite a dry task more challenging we use a fictionalised case study of two people for whom access to community services is particularly problematic. Jim and Marianne are both long-term heroin addicts. Additional problems associated with their addiction are homelessness and physical illness. Their situation raises both practical questions, about how services can be accessed, and moral questions, about entitlement to resources when their problems can be regarded as at least in part self-inflicted.

> **Core questions**
>
> - What barriers are there to access to community health and care services?
> - To what extent can people exercise choice in the services they access?
> - What strategies exist to promote access to services for people who are disadvantaged?

Jim and Marianne's story is based on a real couple, but heavily fictionalised to protect their identity. Their story is a way of tracking the intricacies of the health and care system through the eyes of people for whom it is supposed to work.

The unit is structured around the careers of Jim and Marianne as users of health and social care, but leads out at various points to the structure, philosophy and practice of other services. The unit ends with a discussion of four strategies for change.

Section 1
Jim and Marianne: testing the limits

1.1 Introducing Jim and Marianne

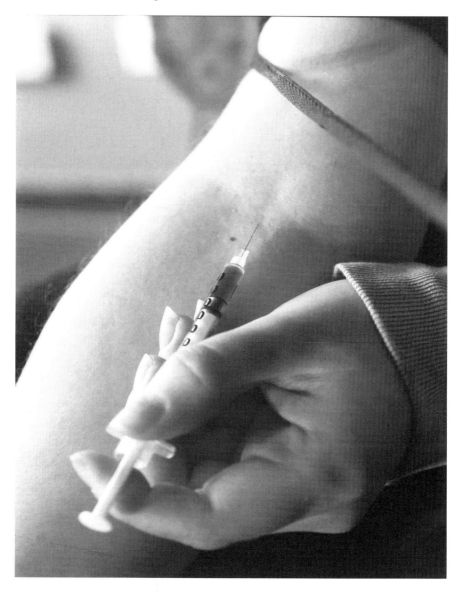

The lifestyles of long-term drug abusers are frequently sensationalised

In the introduction I described Jim and Marianne, our case study for this unit, as 'long-term heroin addicts'. The lifestyles of long-term drug abusers are frequently sensationalised in the media, as in the photograph, and the following extract from *Trainspotting*, a novel about Scottish heroin users that was turned into a hugely successful film:

> *He droaps a cotton ball intae the spoon n blaws oan it, before sucking up aboot 5 mls through the needle, intae the barrel ay the syringe. He's goat a fuckin' huge blue vein tapped up which seems tae be almost comin through Ali's arm. He pierces the flesh and injects a wee bit slowly, before*

suckin blood back intae the chamber. Her lips are quivering as she gazes pleadingly at him for a second or two. Sick Boy's face looks ugly, leering and reptilian, before he slams the cocktail towards her brain.

She pulls back her heid, shuts her eyes and opens her mooth givin' oot an orgasmic groan.

(Welsh, 1993, pp. 8–9)

However, I introduce Jim and Marianne not through a description of such gruesome practices, but through hearing about the people behind the heroin addict label.

Jim and Marianne

Jim and Marianne are a couple. When I met them for the first time they were in their early thirties. They had been together for about ten years. Although they had been having unprotected sex during these years they had no children and Marianne had never become pregnant. They met when they were both in a drug rehabilitation centre on the outskirts of a northern industrial town. They became the 'star pupils' of the centre. They both tried to outdo each other in getting clean from drugs and in striving to become model citizens. They took up all sorts of sporting activities, participated in the groups and in the running of the centre. Eventually, the time to re-enter the community came and they were helped to move into their own flat. Jim was offered a job at the rehabilitation centre itself and Marianne, helped by her family, tried to establish a little business for herself buying and selling things from car boot sales and cheaper antique shops.

Jim described his childhood as 'difficult'. He never knew his father, and he said his mother was unable to cope with him because of her own problems with alcohol. He had spent many of his childhood years in a variety of foster homes and children's homes.

Marianne's parents owned three newsagent shops and were comparatively prosperous. But, according to Marianne, the relationships within her family were not straightforward. Her father had a series of extra-marital affairs, but when his own health deteriorated he came back to be with his wife, Marianne's mother. Their relationship seemed to stabilise but Marianne said they had never been very communicative or demonstrative with each other, or with her, and usually tried to solve problems by spending money on them.

In Jim's words to Marianne:

> *I don't know what's better, my family who fucked me up when I was young, or yours who's always muckin' us about now. They really do my head in. I know they don't like me, and blame me for things. They offer us things, but always with strings attached. I think they want you to leave me, and go back to them.*

The quality of Jim and Marianne's lives deteriorated after a few years out of the rehabilitation centre. Neither of them could sustain the progress they had made. They found that making friends in the community who were not their old 'junkie' friends was very difficult and they became quite socially isolated. Marianne described her family as supportive in some ways, but the emotional costs of getting help from them seemed to be considerable. Jim felt patronised and Marianne felt unable to really confide in either of her parents and was wary of her brothers and their circles of friends. Together Jim and Marianne slipped back into increasing drug use. Jim lost his job immediately at the rehabilitation centre, which insisted on a drug-free environment, and Marianne found it harder than ever to make a living. Both confessed that they were involved in petty crime at this stage. Their general health started to decline. Marianne found that the sites she was using for injection became persistently infected and she spent several spells in hospital with swollen legs and nasty ulcers. Jim had had a valve problem in his heart since birth. His lungs had been damaged by this and by the repeated chest infections he developed. Both of them had hepatitis C infection, which probably contributed to them feeling low in energy and being susceptible to persistent infections.

Activity 1   **The people behind the label**

Allow about 10 minutes   The account in the case study box is about the people behind the drug addict label.

(a)   Did it change your view of them?

(b)   What advantages do you consider such additional knowledge might have for a health practitioner meeting Jim and Marianne for the first time?

(c)   Can you foresee any problems for a practitioner supplied with this additional information?

Comment   (a)   People who read the course varied in their response. Two said emphatically that they did change their views. Another, accustomed to working with people who are often the subject of negative stereotyping, said: 'I would always seek to find the person behind the label'.

(b)   Maybe a practitioner would have more sympathy with Jim and Marianne than if she had simply been presented with bald medical information – intravenous drug user, faulty heart valve, damaged lungs, infertility, subject to persistent low-level infection.

She might be less inclined to make moral judgements such as 'they don't deserve help' or 'they brought it on themselves'.

The additional information might also suggest a broader range of helpful interventions than straightforward medical treatment: family therapy, even fertility treatment for Marianne, whose childlessness was a cause of regret.

(c)   A practitioner might feel overwhelmed by the plethora of problems. It would be much easier, perhaps, to prescribe some antibiotics, give some advice on diet or suggest a detoxification centre.

She might feel that even if she wanted to do more for them, resources were such that she should confine herself to her immediate remit, treatment for the problem as presented.

You may have recognised echoes of the discussion of the biomedical model in Unit 2. It was suggested there that a doctor working in the biomedical framework would probably act differently from one who took a more holistic approach to patients' problems. The next section takes this discussion further by looking at the moral dilemmas a real practitioner faces when coming into contact with people who clearly need help, but who may be classed as 'difficult'.

1.2 Moral dilemmas

It is clear from the account of Jim and Marianne's lives that they need some help. But do they deserve help? Some of our course testers had very strong reactions to the inclusion of drug users in a course about health and social care. Here is one typical response:

> *I am not sure that Jim and Marianne and people like them deserve this sort of attention. Their problems were self-inflicted. It must have cost someone (we taxpayers?) a lot of money to rehabilitate them, yet they wasted the opportunity, cadged more money off Marianne's parents, stole from honest members of the community, and then expected to be bailed out by the NHS. Are there no limits to the obligations we all have to support people who seem determined to waste their lives, and damage the lives of others as they do so?*

Do you share this attitude? It represents a clear challenge to the idea that everyone has rights to health and social care services simply because they happen to be resident in a community.

This question is one we could debate in abstract terms, but it takes a very concrete form when practitioners have to make decisions about resources, eligibility and priorities. Because I take a particular interest in drug users in my work as a GP, I have some experience of facing the issues. I explore some of them in Chapter 5 in the Reader.

Activity 2 **Tough decisions**

Allow about 20 minutes

Read Chapter 5 in the Reader now. Concentrate on the dilemmas I faced in considering what to do when called out by Julia to examine her child. As this block is about communities, look at the question from two perspectives:

(a)   the GP's obligations to the individual

(b)   the GP's obligations to the community

and, under these headings, list the considerations involved in coming to a decision about taking Julia and her family on to the practice list.

Comment

Obligations to the individual	Obligations to the community
Sick child, no fault of his own	Family will be expensive to treat, means fewer resources to spend on other (more deserving?) patients
Holistic view of Julia's situation suggests she needs help	Doctors should focus on things they can treat rather than trying to take on the troubles of the world
Julia is asking for help for the first time, responding to an empathetic doctor	Should not reward a deviant who has brought her troubles on her own head
May be an opportunity to stop this family sliding deeper into the mire	May be a constant drain on public money with no real return

No other agencies available to offer support	Democratically elected local authority has taken the decision to withdraw helping agencies; doctor should go with this consensus

In theory, everyone has the right to register with a GP practice, and expect treatment – something we examine in more detail below. There are other things to think about too.

- It is not just Julia whose welfare is at stake: her children may be at some kind of risk. Any health or social care worker in contact with Julia's family will have to be aware of the Children Act 1989 principle that 'the child's welfare is paramount' (Department of Health, 1989a), and act accordingly. In the case of the GP this will mean checking with the health visitors attached to the practice, and asking them to visit. They will be obliged to take action if Julia is not providing the care that a 'reasonable parent' should supply under the circumstances.

- In this sort of situation a GP may be professionally liable if things were to go wrong and the child became seriously ill as a result of negligence.

- On this occasion my own needs, and those of my family, had to be put aside, but neither a GP nor any other health or social care worker can sustain this level of commitment to the welfare of others indefinitely.

- In the Reader chapter I also reflect on why I am attracted to work with drug users. Is it solely out of altruism, or does this aspect of my work feed an unworthy personal need? And does that matter?

This chapter shows that just one small encounter can present a practitioner like me with a whole host of moral dilemmas. It is well nigh impossible to draw hard and fast rules when every case is different, and when personal as well as professional issues come into play. Legal requirements, such as the Children Act, mean that the question is not just a matter of individual judgement.

Moreover, such decisions have to be made not only at the face-to-face level, but in planning how to use limited resources.

Activity 3　Rationing resources

Allow about 5 minutes　As a member of a health authority responsible for purchasing health services you are faced with a contracting budget. Given a choice between retaining an eight-bed drug rehabilitation centre (where someone like Julia could get treatment) and setting up four additional beds for acute psychiatric care, which would you choose?

Comment　This dilemma was faced by one health authority in 1997. The decision was to close the drug rehabilitation centre in favour of financing acute psychiatric care. Did you make the same choice?

If you did make the decision that Jim and Marianne, Julia and her children, are less deserving than people with acute psychiatric conditions, where would you draw the line? At treatment for motorists who drink or drive recklessly; cyclists who do not wear helmets; smokers; people who eat too much fatty food, or indulge in sports like ski-ing or horse riding, which carry a high risk of injury?

If you knew that a place in prison, where many drug users spend time, costs up to £30,000 a year, would that influence your decision?

1.3 Testing the limits

Choosing Jim and Marianne as the central case study in the unit was a deliberate strategy to enable you to consider conflicts at the very heart of health and social care:

• the rights of the individual versus the rights of the community

• the nature of community for people who have no settled abode

• dilemmas about apportioning limited resources.

Following their story is a way of testing the limits of health and social care services, and exploring where community obligation should stop.

There are considerable moral and ethical issues involved in the debates around this case study. Do citizens have unlimited calls on health service resources, or are there limits to what services and facilities people could or should expect from the state? Do people whose problems may be considered to be 'self-inflicted' have the same rights and access to resources as other people? We will be reconsidering such questions at various points in the unit.

Key points

• An approach that seeks to find the person behind the label is an antidote to their being seen simply as a collection of 'problems'. It may also make a practitioner's task more complex.

• Heavy drug users test the limits of community services.

• Practitioners and planners are faced with moral dilemmas that are not susceptible to hard and fast rules.

• When children are involved, the welfare of the adult patient or client is not the sole consideration.

Study skills: Reading towards your essays

With TMA 02 only just behind you, perhaps it seems untimely to raise the topic of assignments now. Yet, as you launch yourself into another block, this is a good moment to stop and think about how your essay writing fits into your studies as a whole. Did your recent essay feel like a last-minute panic, or had you been building up to it gradually during the previous weeks? Are there ways to build essay writing into your work on the whole block?

One possibility is to look at TMA 03 right now. The questions on offer may not make complete sense to you before you have read the block, but you can still try underlining key words in pencil and start jotting down a few thoughts straight away. This will focus your mind and help you to recognise what might be useful for your essay as you work through the units. If you have an 'Essay' folder, then, as you study the block, you can keep adding in new ideas as you jot them down. Then, by the time you reach the writing stage, you will have a good basis from which to build your essay. Also, having the essay titles in mind will give you a stronger sense of purpose as you read. It will also help to shape your ideas and opinions, so that they are more fully developed when you need them for writing your essay.

It would be wrong to see the whole course as shackled to the essays, or to regard what is not relevant to the essays as not worth knowing. But being aware of the essay questions gives an extra thrust to your studies – a purpose to your reading and an edge against which to hone your thoughts. As we said earlier, writing essays is a key part of the learning process, and you can make it work for you all the way through each block.

See Section 11.2.3 of Chapter 11 of *The Good Study Guide* (p. 301).

Section 2
Accessing primary care

This section is about gaining access to primary care, one service that is open to every member of the population as of right. First, we pick up Jim and Marianne's story again.

Homeless

Jim and Marianne's problems worsened when they became homeless. It happened like this.

Jim and Marianne decided to move away from their old haunts and try to make a new start in Sheffield. Marianne's parents gave them the deposit on a small flat above a chip shop and also the first week's rent. Marianne said that her mother wanted them to have the money but her father was resistant, saying that it would just get wasted, as it had been all the other times they had given them anything in the past.

Unfortunately, her father was proved right. Jim and Marianne were not used to having so much cash in hand; they spent most of the money on heroin and were evicted. They found a place to sleep and store their few possessions in an old potting shed at the corner of a disused allotment on the edge of town. But conditions deteriorated with the onset of autumn. The ground was muddy around the shed and they thought they had been spotted by one of the Allotment Committee members. Jim's chest started to play up again, he began coughing up horrible green stuff, and became quite low and unmotivated in his mood. Marianne's leg ulcers took a turn for the worse.

They decided to get their health sorted out properly ...

2.1 What is primary care?

Jim and Marianne's first and most obvious port of call is their GP surgery. Even people who have little local knowledge usually know that there will be a doctor's practice locally. Jim and Marianne find that the GP practises in a modern purpose-built health centre. The Information Booklet in the waiting area tells them that it supplies 'primary care services' and that there are four other GPs in the practice, which serves the suburbs and the villages beyond. In addition to the GPs, the staff comprises:

- a practice manager
- three clerks/receptionists
- two practice nurses
- a counsellor who works three days a week at the centre.

The practice also supplies on-site physiotherapy, chiropody, minor operations and child psychiatry from professionals who visit at regular intervals.

A health centre

What the booklet did not explain, because it is assumed that everyone knows the answer, is what is meant by 'primary care services'.

Primary care

Although the booklet in the surgery assumed most people know what is meant by the term 'primary care', an exact definition can be surprisingly hard to pin down. Barbara Starfield, an American public health academic, has proposed this definition:

> *Primary care is first-contact, continuous, comprehensive, and co-ordinated care provided to populations undifferentiated by gender, disease, or organ system...*
>
> *(Starfield, 1994, p. 1129)*

This differentiates primary care from 'secondary' services usually provided within hospitals. In addition to this definition Starfield has described the four functions of primary care that together define it uniquely:

> *These four functions are the point of first contact for all new needs, person focus rather than disease focussed care over time, providing care for **all** needs that are common in the population, and co-ordinating care for both those needs and for needs that are sufficiently uncommon to require special services.*
>
> *(Starfield, 1995, p. 3)*

The box summarises the advantages and disadvantages of each of these functions as they operate in the UK.

The four functions of primary care

First point of contact for all new needs

The existence of a practice list, whereby most people in the UK have a named GP, ensures that entry to secondary services is controlled. Compared with direct entry to specialist services, as happens in some other countries, this method is cost-effective. Self-referral to specialist services can lead to expensive duplication of investigations and even unnecessary surgical intervention (Franks *et al.*, 1992). Potential disadvantages might include denial of referral to a relevant specialist or refusal to consider the need for a second opinion.

Person focus rather than disease-focused care over time

Person-focused care is said to lead to better recognition of people's problems, more consistent preventive care, better communication between physician and consulting person, less inappropriate use and less hospitalisation ... and more satisfaction all round. Possible disadvantages are that a generalist (GP) might miss a serious illness, which would have been spotted by a specialist who was focusing on disease manifestation rather than on the person.

Providing care for all needs that are common in the population

This has many obvious advantages. A comprehensive service serves the needs of the whole population. Even when there may be competing demands on resources, a unified service can ensure a rational evaluation of those demands. Possible disadvantages might be that no single person or service can know everything about all conditions ... is it all spread a little thin this way?

Co-ordinating care for primary care needs and for needs that require special services

Co-ordinating care ensures that the primary care workers are aware of special referrals that are made and assist in making them, and provide information that helps the specialist come to the correct conclusions. When information is returned from the specialist this can be discussed with the person who has attended. The benefits include greater efficiency of care and less likelihood of adverse effects resulting from incompatible recommendations and treatments. Possible disadvantages are that the system relies on good communication between specialist and primary care services, and, if for any reason the individual is denied access to primary care services, they will have great difficulty accessing other more specialist medical services.

Activity 4   **The functions of primary care**

Allow about 20 minutes   Using the information in 'The four functions of primary care' box to guide you, write a few notes on the possible advantages and disadvantages of each of the four functions of primary care as far as Jim and Marianne are concerned:

(a) first point of contact for all new needs

(b) person focus rather than disease-focused care over time

(c) providing care for all needs that are common in the population

(d) co-ordinating care for primary care needs and for needs that require special services.

Comment   (a) *First point of contact for all new needs.* Jim and Marianne know where to go for their health needs (as you will see this is not necessarily the case with community care services). They won't feel singled out because the service is used by almost everyone. The disadvantage is that if they meet an unhelpful or judgmental response, their access to other services or specialist forms of medical care might be barred.

(b) *Person focus rather than disease-focused care over time.* You may have considered this in the discussion of the person behind the label in Section 1. Jim and Marianne seem to need people within the formal services who can appreciate them as individuals, rather than who simply respond to their immediate medical needs. It would be easy to see them as a collection of symptoms and pathologies, and miss the point that they are human beings who need medical treatment because of a complex interplay of factors. However, they might prefer to have only their medical symptoms attended to, rather than have their whole lives opened to scrutiny by strangers.

(c) *Providing care for all needs that are common in the population.* Can one service even begin to meet everyone's needs? Jim and Marianne's needs are not especially common, particularly in the leafy suburb where their surgery is situated.

(d) *Co-ordinating care for primary care needs and for needs that require special services.* For Jim and Marianne, having a central co-ordinating primary care service could be enormously helpful. It ensures, for example, that the various hospital services they require report back to a single place. All their hospital reports will come back to the health centre and the workers there will be able to review their current state of health at any time. On the other hand, if they are unfortunate in their choice of GP, or cannot get one at all, they might lose out entirely.

You may well not recognise the service you get from your GP in this description of primary care, because in many cases it represents an ideal to be aspired to, rather than reality. In the rest of the section you will see whether this ideal works for Jim and Marianne.

The ideal GP?

2.2 Patients' rights and responsibilities

One of the implications of the primary care model is that GPs control access to a range of medical services. They perform a 'gate-keeping' function, determining whether someone should get specialist treatment. Indeed, in order to be eligible for some state benefits, such as Incapacity Benefit, a doctor's signature to a statement of medical need is a prerequisite. For people in need of health care, getting on to a GP list is obviously crucial. Technically this should not be a problem, because the NHS has set out certain rights and responsibilities for patients. Interestingly the emphasis and rhetoric about the interaction between people and 'their' NHS has changed recently. The emphasis on patients' rights, which were enshrined in the previous 'Patient's Charter' (Association of Community Health Councils for England and Wales, 1994), has been replaced in more recent documents by a need for a balance between a new form of words setting out both what the NHS expects of patients... and then what patients can expect from the NHS (Department of Health, 2001a, b, & c).

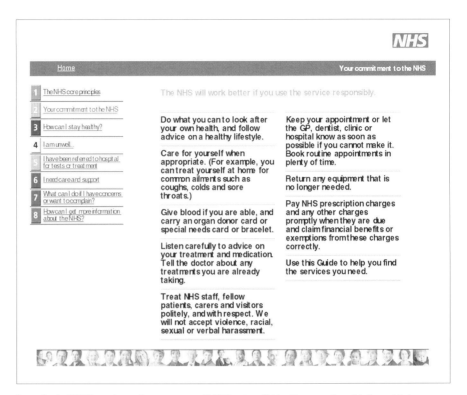

In today's NHS patients have responsibilities too (http://www.nhs.uk/nhsguide/ 2_yr_cmmtmnt.htm [accessed 27.5.02])

As I said above, unlike most of the services in health and social care you have encountered so far in the course, primary care is available to all. It has the great advantage of being universal. Almost everyone, white or black, rich or poor, old or young, can use primary care services. There is no stigma attached to going to your doctor, as there often is to, say, approaching a clinic for sexually transmitted diseases, being a child 'in care' or attending a psychiatric service.

But you might like to reflect on the force of some of these 'rights'. You have a right to be registered, provided that the doctor agrees to accept you – but the GP also has a right to refuse you, and does not have to justify his or her refusal.

It could be considered that not only are patients' rights restricted in practice, but also they only cover a limited range of interactions.

Activity 5   Receiving Jim and Marianne

Allow about 10 minutes   What response might Jim and Marianne get when approaching a primary care centre you know? Try to base your responses on your own experiences of local services rather than on stereotypical views.

Comment   Our course testers thought that there would be a great range of issues raised and potential responses. Some predicted a thoroughly negative and potentially hostile response, while others thought they would be treated in the same way as any other people seeking help:

> *'Our local team always seems so warm and inviting to all comers. I expect Jim and Marianne would get a similar welcome.'*

> *'It all depends who is on the desk and who they get to meet. Some of the staff and doctors are wonderful, but others I should think would make their lives pretty uncomfortable.'*

'I've recently moved and had difficulty finding a doctor because they are so territorial. How would J and M manage without an address?'

'Practice boundaries have tightened. My downstairs neighbour's doctor refused me as 'out of his area'. The reception at my new doctor's was rather like immigration control when I signed on. The woman in front of me, who was black, was registering for herself and her sister (currently out of the country). She was being asked very detailed questions about places and dates of residence for herself and her sister and being quoted prices in case she had to pay. Presumably it wasn't a racist thing as neither of the practice doctors is white.'

'Our doctors and their team would make sure that they knew that they were unwelcome, largely because they will be so costly to treat. They would try to get shot of them by making them feel stigmatised and just about frozen out.'

So, new patients cannot always be sure of a warm welcome. Below, we examine some factors that influence people's ability to access primary care.

2.3 Geography, attitudes and resources

In practice, people like Jim and Marianne can have great difficulty in exercising their 'rights' to primary health care. The responses to Activity 5 refer to three factors that will make their right to access the primary care service problematic:

- geography
- attitudes
- resources.

Each of these is examined in turn.

Geography

Difficulty in accessing services is partly a matter of where people live. Despite good intentions such as 'Services should not vary widely in range or quality in different parts of the country' (Department of Health, 1996, p. 8), inner-city areas often have far lower standards of primary care than the medical centre described earlier; often a GP will be working single-handedly in poorly adapted premises.

In addition, any practice will almost certainly restrict access on the grounds of where people live. Most practices have a catchment area. Beyond this circumscribed area it is considered impractical to take on new patients because of possible problems with, for example, home visiting.

Homeless people like Jim and Marianne have particular difficulty registering with services that are based on the notion of a geographical community with spatial boundaries. We considered the significance of homelessness in Unit 6. Not having an address is a real problem when almost all registration processes require it. A 1996 report for Shelter, the voluntary organisation concerned with providing decent housing for all, showed that while 97 per cent of the population as a whole are registered with a GP, approximately 70 per cent of homeless people were not. Reasons cited by respondents were that they were told the doctor's list was full, or they were not allowed to fill in the forms by the receptionist. As a result, the report shows, most homeless people rely on hospital accident and emergency services for health care, with the result that they do not get a co-ordinated response or access to other services that primary care provides. As one care worker interviewed for the survey commented:

> The problem is that the GP is the gatekeeper to the NHS these days – if you haven't got a doctor you're in trouble.

> (North et al., 1996, p. 5)

Attitudes

As our course testers' responses to Activity 5 suggest, not all teams or individual health professionals have a positive attitude towards treating people with drug-related problems. Some of the barriers to GP involvement have been identified in various reports.

A survey of GPs in Greater Manchester (Davies and Huxley, 1997) reported that 20 per cent of GPs did not prescribe for opiate users; 11 per cent believed that opiate users should be removed from the practice list; and 45 per cent believed that treatment of opiate users was beyond the competence of GPs. Drug users themselves may be reluctant to register with a GP because they see them as unsympathetic (McKeganey, 1988). In a study in Scotland (Greenwood, 1992) other reasons given included GPs' difficulty in establishing rapport and fears of being taken advantage of, the potential for deceit, disgust at injecting practices, fear of contracting HIV, fear of censure from colleagues for substitute prescribing, possible effect on other patients in the practice and disillusionment at patients' relapses.

Implicit value judgements might also be made.

- Are these people going to be time-consuming, 'demanding' or problematic to the practice? The fear might be that they will use up an excessive amount of the energies of the staff.

- Is there a threat of violence or disruptive behaviour? Many people's views of drug users are stereotypical and those who come into contact with them may initially imagine that they will be more violent than other people.

- Might drug users somehow affect the experience of other people who attend the health centre? If there are large numbers of drug users on the premises, might this make other attenders feel threatened or less comfortable in some way?

These are all fears that many providers of health care services might share. They are not necessarily borne out by research. For example, although there are increasing reports of violence perpetrated on primary care staff (Kidd and Stark, 1995), there is no evidence that this is particularly due to people with drug-related problems. There is, however, evidence that drug users do use primary care services more often than people who do not use opiates (Leaver *et al.*, 1992).

Resources

Jim and Marianne are likely to need more than average amounts of drugs, person time, hospital referrals and the like. We made a start on listing their medical needs in Activity 1. Just to remind you, medical support might involve:

- infertility advice
- cardiology referral for Jim's heart
- nursing help with Marianne's ulcers
- liver specialist referral for their hepatitis problems.

There can be no avoiding the fact that any primary care team Jim and Marianne approach for help will be aware that becoming involved with them will involve a considerable commitment of time, energy and expense.

Such issues have acquired more urgency as greater emphasis is placed on costing services supplied through primary care. Many arrangements for organising and delivering primary care services introduced in the late 1980s and 1990s had as their explicit purpose the need to control and keep account of the costs of the services provided. The intention was to make all GPs and other members of primary health care teams aware of the costs of the facilities that are under their control, or to which they might wish to make referrals. For example, all doctors receive a monthly statement of the amount that they have spent on medication, how this compares with their expenditure in the previous year and how it compares with other doctors' expenditure, both in their own area and nationally. Also, many Primary Care Groups restrict the amount that primary health care teams can spend on the salaries of the people working in the team, and there are controls on other items of primary care expenditure.

Improving patient access to information

In recent years the NHS has made various attempts to provide easier access to information about all their available services. Most recently these include a single point of entry information system called NHS Direct, which can be contacted either by telephone (0845 4647) or on the web: www.nhsdirect.nhs.uk [accessed 27.5.02].

Information about government policies regarding the NHS is also readily available using: www.doh.gov.uk [accessed 27.5.02].

> There is also a new system of patient advocacy services being established. These will replace existing Community Health Councils. People will be able to access the new advocacy services through local 'Patient Advice and Liaison Services (PALS)'.
>
> *'PALS are central to the new system of patient and public involvement ... Providing information and on the spot help for patients, their families and carers, they will be a powerful level for change and improvement.'*
>
> *http://www.doh.gov.uk/patientadviceandliasonservices/index.htm [accessed 27.5.02].*

It is not hard to imagine that new people joining the practice list, such as Jim and Marianne, could be seen as significant challenges to already limited resources. Certainly, compared with others applying to join the list, they may well require more staff resources, more money spent on their medication and may also require a series of referrals to other agencies. The income that is generated for the practice by two people joining the list, however, is not dependent on their clinical needs. So the practice will be paid exactly the same amount for Jim and Marianne as for any other couple of the same age, living in the same area.

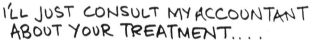

The ideal of community services for all is in theory met by the way primary care services are organised in the UK. But issues of geography, attitudes and resources mean that in practice the ideal is not always the reality.

2.4 Jim and Marianne: experiences of primary care

We have spent some time considering factors that might influence how Jim and Marianne, and others like them whom services perceive as 'difficult', are received by primary care services. So what actually happened?

Here is what Jim and Marianne had to say when asked about their experiences of approaching various GP practices:

[Jim speaking] Over the years we have had a really wide range of responses from the different GPs we have had to approach. I know we look rather rough these days, but we are not stupid. When I was working in the rehab house I used to go along to various health centres with the clients from there and act as their advocate, so I do know what I am talking about. But sometimes you are just treated like something the cat has just brought in. It is demoralising and just makes me feel even worse about myself than before. All the time I get nervous about what I should say and I end up feeling tense. Most of the time I would just rather not go. Many of them [GPs] are just bastards, and they don't want us mucking up their clean carpets.

[Marianne] We've been in just about all the hospitals in the area over the years, and tried out quite a few GPs too. It's difficult when they get to know you're using. I always think people are talking about us. The nurses and receptionists sometimes put you at the back of the queue, you watch everyone going in before you. Sometimes, when I'm in a bad way, I don't think it's worth the bother.

But when you do get a good one, one you can sort of settle down with, that's really good. They are not all crap, but even with the good ones you are a bit on edge wondering if you have said the right thing and sort of apologising just for being there at all.

You'll recall the discussion in Unit 4 of doctor–patient scripts, and the power doctors appear to exert in defining what is, and what is not, permissible behaviour in a consultation. Even once Jim and Marianne had penetrated the barriers to entering the presence of the doctor, it seems that some doctors were well defended against being overwhelmed by, or even sympathetic to, their predicament.

There is a tension between enabling the users of services to access the services they need and the competing imperative to control, manage and contain services within a managerial and cost-limited framework. This tension is apparent in the struggle that Jim and Marianne may have in obtaining satisfactory help with their problems, even in a service such as primary care, which sets out to be available to each and every member of the community.

How far might the barriers identified in relation to Jim and Marianne apply to anyone? Some of the issues thrown up by their story are peculiar to people who are seen as difficult or deviant, but the geographical basis of primary care can present problems to people moving house, while any patient depends heavily on the skill and willingness to listen of the GP, the crucial gatekeeper to a range of health services.

Section 3 explores some issues in accessing community care services, which, unlike primary care, do not aspire to be universal.

Key points

- Primary health care is defined as first contact, continuous, comprehensive and co-ordinated care provided to all.

- Primary health care is available as of right to everyone resident in the UK. Nevertheless, some 'deviant' groups, such as drug users, may find it hard in practice to get accepted on to a GP's list. Even moving house can be a barrier.

- A health care system that depends on primary care as the first and co-ordinating point of contact has advantages in terms of accessibility to the majority of the population but, for some disadvantaged groups, it may also be a barrier to obtaining medical help.

- Services that serve geographical communities are hard for homeless people to access.

- Primary health care teams vary in their approach to their patients – access may depend too much on the personal philosophy of the GP.

- Moves to make expenditure on health care the responsibility of individual practices mean that primary health care teams may be reluctant to take on patients who appear to be expensive to treat.

Section 3
Accessing community care

This section asks what issues individuals like Jim and Marianne may encounter as they try to access care in the community in which they happen to live.

First of all, we catch up with Jim and Marianne's story again, as they move from being patients of primary care to becoming users of community care services.

Crisis

Unfortunately, things did not work out well for Jim and Marianne. Jim's defective heart valve became infected (sub-acute bacterial endocarditis) and an infected embolus was thrown from the aortic valve into the left side of his brain. He had a stroke, which affected his speech and many functions on the right-hand side of his body.

Marianne said:

> I thought Jim was gonna die, he looked that awful. He lost even more weight and looked kind of sick yellow, you could see the bones in his face. Anyone looking at him would think he's got AIDS or something. He walks funny and talks like he's drunk all the time. He keeps getting in moods, fighting with the doctors.

Marianne was no luckier. The injection site in her right groin failed to heal. She had increasing problems injecting there, but all her other veins were thrombosed long before. During a particularly problematic injecting session, while she was tired and anxious about Jim, she punctured her left femoral artery. This in turn thrombosed and she was rushed to hospital, where it was decided to amputate ...

At one stage both Jim and Marianne were in hospital at the same time. Jim was in the Stroke Rehabilitation Unit, based in a small community hospital. He made good progress. His speech returned almost completely, although he still slurred some words, making him sound rather drunk when he was tired. His mood was affected and he was often sullen and withdrawn and easily became irritable and verbally aggressive. Although he could move around inside the unit, using items of furniture for support, he was not really strong enough to venture out on his own: he could not cross roads or carry shopping. Marianne was under the care of specialist vascular surgeons who amputated her right leg at thigh level. For her period of rehabilitation and intensive physiotherapy, while waiting for her new limb to be fitted, she was transferred to the District General Hospital. Unfortunately, because the amputation was necessarily at a very high level through her right hip, she was unable, finally, to use her prosthesis and was told she would have to use a wheelchair for the rest of her life.

'What a pair we are', said Marianne immediately after her amputation. 'To think we used to be fit and healthy. We biked everywhere. Up the big hills and all. What a way to live. I wouldn't do it to a dog.'

3.1 Entering the system

In this section we examine some of the barriers to accessing good-quality community care that Jim and Marianne might experience. Unlike the world of primary health care, with which she and Jim were all too familiar, community care was a new concept to Marianne. I am going to take you through some of the issues she and Jim are likely to encounter as they cross from primary health care services that (almost) everyone uses to services reserved for that minority of adults who need extra help.

We pick up Jim and Marianne's story at the point they were discharged from hospital. Although they entered hospital with the label of substance abusers or drug addicts, when they left they had in practice entered a new category from a service provider's point of view, that of people with impaired mobility. Jim was not really strong enough to get out and about or carry shopping, and Marianne was in a wheelchair. In a sense, they made the transition from being, perhaps, marginal to social care to being physically disabled, one of the classic groups for whom community care provides. Ironically, you might argue that in community care terms Marianne was fortunate to have her leg amputated. Not only did it save her life, it also meant that she qualified for assistance under the Chronically Sick and Disabled Persons Act 1970, which makes it a duty of local authorities to make an assessment of a person deemed to be disabled, whether or not they request it. If she had remained able-bodied she would merely be, in the eyes of the law, homeless, and might, at worst, have been discharged from hospital to make her own way on the streets. Jim's position is more ambiguous. He might qualify in his own right – he might also expect support if he were to be designated as Marianne's carer. You will recall from Unit 1, Section 3, that the Carers (Recognition and Services) Act 1995 requires the needs of carers to be the subject of a separate assessment if requested.

What can they expect now that they are part of community care?

First, it will be helpful to refresh your memory about how community care is intended to operate under the NHS and Community Care Act 1990 (see Care Systems and Structures). From the user's point of view key aims of the new system were:

- to enable people to live as independently as possible in their own homes or 'homely' settings in the community (Department of Health, 1989b, p. 3)

- 'to give people a greater say ... in how they live their lives and the services they need to help them to do so' (Department of Health, 1989b, p. 4)

- to enable users and carers to 'exercise the same power as consumers of other services' (Social Services Inspectorate/Scottish Social Work Group, 1991, p. 11).

In other words, the central aims were to give users of the system more power to make choices, something that has loosely been termed 'empowerment'. How far are Jim and Marianne likely to be able to realise these ideals? First, we look at some difficulties they might have in obtaining information. Then we look at barriers in the process of needs assessment.

empowerment → to make people have their own choices.

3.2 Obtaining information: community care plans

One place to which Jim and Marianne might turn for information about their rights and entitlements, now they are community care users, is the community care plan which all social services departments up until recently were obliged to develop and publish. Most social services and social work (Scotland) departments still have these in place and are likely to well into the foreseeable future, when they will be replaced by a range of other documents that lay out the rights and entitlements that users can expect.

Activity 6	Community care plans

Allow about 20 minutes

Offprint 14 is an extract from one local authority's 1996/7 community care plan. In fact, Jim and Marianne might fit into any one of three service user categories in the plan – 'Services for people with mental health problems', 'Services for people with drug or alcohol problems' or 'Services for people with disabilities'. We have reprinted only the third of these, as Jim and Marianne entered the system with the 'disabilities' label. Read Offprint 14 now, then use your knowledge of Jim and Marianne to make an assessment of how useful it might be to them as a basis for knowledge of what they can expect as newcomers to community care services.

Comment

I imagine Jim and Marianne might find the document less than helpful. For a start, a lot of the information is about people with learning disabilities, numerically the largest single group of users, and is irrelevant to them. Second, I wondered how they would find the language. Abbreviations such as 'F and CS' (Family and Community Services [Department]), although explained in the Introduction to the plan, are obscure, and there are a number of other jargon terms, such as 'Single Regeneration Budget' and 'integrated care management'.

The paragraph headed 'Assessment and care management' gives no useful information to people like Jim and Marianne, except perhaps to illuminate any problems they may be experiencing as they are handed from health to social services managed provision.

The paragraph headed 'Home support services' may indicate that they can expect some kind of help in their home, if and when they get one, and the following paragraph on 'Equipment and adaptations' is similar. But neither the range of assistance they can expect nor the process for obtaining it is spelt out in enough detail to be of practical assistance.

'Day time services' is again largely concerned with learning disability services. It is unlikely that the brief description of options outlined for those with physical disabilities will attract Jim and Marianne.

'Respite care' may in time seem to be important, but there is no obvious 'carer' here. I suggested that Jim might eventually come to see himself as a 'carer', but it is very early days for this to seem a likely option.

'Housing' should be of prime interest. Again, the plan gives very little useful information to people in Jim and Marianne's position.

'Health services' is an area Jim and Marianne know well. Perhaps they might like to know whether they can turn to their primary care service for help. There is no answer here.

One of the aims of the 1990 community care reforms was to provide a mechanism for consultation, collaboration and better provision of information for people who use services and their carers. A principal means of doing this was through publication of an annually revised community care plan.

In preparing a community care plan a social services authority had to:

- consult with a number of bodies, including any voluntary bodies that appear to represent users and carers

- ensure that information about community care services is easily available

- ensure that such information is made available in a form that is readily understandable.

However, Gwyneth Roberts, in reviewing community care plans, argues that there is uncertainty about the audiences for whom the plans are designed. One purpose is to aid the local authority's business planning (something you'll read more about in Block 6), and the other is to provide the public with information. In practice, these two purposes are pretty incompatible, and she writes that most community care plans are 'barely accessible to the general population' – let alone people with low levels of literacy, or poor concentration, who make up quite a proportion of users of community care services (Roberts, 1996, p. 158). She found that few plans were available in minority languages, or in Braille or on audio tape or video.

The plan illustrated in Offprint 14 is by no means the worst plan we found. It was not published in any language other than English, but the Community Care Charter included in it is translated into five other languages. However, it seems to fall short of meeting its purpose of providing the sort of information that will enable Jim and Marianne to make informed choices.

What of the assessment process? Will that offer them choices?

3.3 The assessment process

Of course, Jim and Marianne won't be on their own in finding out about services, nor will they be able to access them without a 'needs assessment', a process you read about in Unit 3. During Marianne's stay in hospital the social services department was informed that she was in need of a community care assessment. Marianne was allocated to a care manager whose job was to conduct a needs assessment. A needs assessment is intended to offer service users the opportunity to exercise informed choice:

> Assessment is ... a key part of the process of translating the general duty to provide or arrange community care services within a particular area into a specific service or package of services for a particular individual.

> (Roberts, 1996, p. 159)

Carried out properly, with the right sort of relationship and information at hand, and access to suitable and adequate resources, assessment has the potential to play a key role in offering choice. However, there are problems as far as people like Jim and Marianne are concerned. We examine these now.

SHEFFIELD'S
COMMUNITY CARE SERVICES

SERVICE CHARTER

*A*ll the agencies who are involved in Community Care in Sheffield want to make sure that you get the best quality services that can be provided with the resources available. All the providers in Sheffield have agreed to publish charters, so you'll know what kind of service you can expect to receive.

We believe it is important that you have a clear idea of what standards you can expect from Community Care services. For this reason we are publishing a statement which sets out in general terms what we are trying to achieve.

The rights and expectations under the Charter are broken down into six standards. These are described in detail in a leaflet available from F&CS Information Services, telephone 273 4969. Listed below are the main points under the six Charter Standards:

As a service user, you have the right to expect:

- ▶ To be treated fairly with courtesy and respect for your dignity, privacy, cultural and religious beliefs.

- ▶ To be consulted and have your views considered, and to have information provided treated in confidence.

- ▶ To have clear information regarding the services provided, in languages other than English and formats other than print.

- ▶ To ask for an assessment of your needs.

- ▶ To be consulted as part of the assessment process, have your views considered and ask for a review of the assessment.

- ▶ To be able to comment or complain about services.

- ▶ Prompt remedial action if services do not come up to the standards laid down.

And as a service user, we expect you:

- ▶ To notify the provider as quickly as possible if you for any reason have to cancel an appointment.

- ▶ To behave courteously and reasonably towards other service users and towards employees and contractors.

These rights and expectations form the main points of the Community Care Charter. For a leaflet giving full details of the Standards under the Community Care Charter contact F&CS Information Services, telephone 273 4969.

Community Care Charters are being published by all the following organisations in Sheffield - Family and Community Services Department, Housing Department, Sheffield Health Authority, Community Health Sheffield, South Yorkshire Probation Service, Sheffield Hospital Trusts, and Private, Charitable and Voluntary organisations throughout the city.

Sheffield's community care services charter

'Ordinarily resident'

Many of the duties and powers of local authorities to assess arise only in relation to those 'ordinarily resident' in the area (Roberts, 1996, p. 163). As Jim and Marianne moved into the area only a year or so earlier it might be argued that they were someone else's responsibility.

This could lead to unseemly wrangles between the local authority where they now live and the local authority where they came from, and where Marianne's family still live, as to who picks up the bill. Where two local authorities are in disagreement about 'ordinary residence' only the Secretary of State can finally decide. Jim and Marianne have no right in law to insist on staying in the area if they want or need community care services.

Backlog of cases

Jim and Marianne are likely to have to wait for a full assessment.

It is not uncommon to have to wait for up to six months for a specialist assessment by an occupational therapist. Without an assessment quite simple aids, such as bath boards or bath seats, are unavailable, which means that domiciliary staff, such as home care assistants, are unable to carry out their jobs (Hadley and Clough, 1996, p. 78).

In law, it is possible for users of community care services to make a formal complaint about failure to assess, or even take the matter to court through a process known as 'judicial review'. However, few people have the know-how or financial resources to make this right a reality, even if they have the energy.

Marianne did get an early assessment because she was 'bed-blocking' in hospital, and she was given priority so that her bed could be used by another patient. But for many new and existing users of services a full and comprehensive assessment may mean a long wait.

Lack of knowledge that an assessment is going on

There is evidence that when care managers undertake assessments, the people on the receiving end are unaware of the significance of the meeting. John Baldock and Clare Ungerson, who conducted research into the experiences of stroke victims (like Jim) who were assessed for community care services after leaving hospital, found that of their 32 respondents only two knew they had had an assessment, what it was for, and who their care manager was. The meetings, which in the eyes of the multidisciplinary teams constituted assessments and at which the users and their relatives were present, were not recognised as such. Consequently, any opportunity to raise questions or ask for services or specific forms of assistance was wasted. Only two new users successfully negotiated the system, and both of these had been employed in public services in the past (Baldock and Ungerson, 1994, Chapter 2).

In other words, the assessment process is a mystery to many of those involved in it.

An ongoing process?

A cursory examination of Jim and Marianne's history suggests that their 'needs' changed over time. While they were in the rehabilitation hostel, their needs were for gainful employment; on leaving hospital, their needs were far more basic – a home, money, help in adjusting to new physical limitations. To work properly, assessment needs to be ongoing, not a one-off event.

Resource constraints

A care manager is expected to bear in mind resource constraints when assembling a care package. Of course, these vary from place to place and time to time. But this is a very real headache when it comes to starting from scratch, as any care manager working with Jim and Marianne will have to do. To illustrate this, we'll consider their housing needs. Obviously, housing is a pressing need, without which little can be done. But the information on housing in the community care plan was, to say the least, sketchy. Now try your hand at listing the problems Jim, Marianne and their care manager are likely to face when it comes to housing, making use of information in Unit 6, Section 2.

Activity 7   **Housing for Jim and Marianne**

Allow about 20 minutes   Re-read Unit 6, Section 2, then make a list of the problems you foresee in
    providing housing suited to Jim and Marianne's needs. Note any additional
problems you can think of which are not mentioned there.

Comment   I noted the following:

- Most housing is designed for able-bodied people. There is likely to be a shortage of 'special needs housing'. I also noted that, because Jim and Marianne are disabled in different ways, the likelihood of finding housing suitable for both of them is even less.

- Most accommodation for people like Jim and Marianne is likely to be in specialist facilities where 'care' is also supplied. Jim and Marianne may not want this, as they have been accustomed to a good deal of freedom of movement. Also, would they be treated as a couple or would Marianne be offered a place in a hostel, leaving Jim to fend for himself on the streets?

* Housing needs are to be dealt with as part of a needs assessment, but most housing is the responsibility of housing departments. In Unit 6 it was noted that planning and communication between housing and social services departments are often poor. Teamworking will be essential if Jim and Marianne are to get a home that meets their physical needs.

An additional problem not mentioned in Unit 6 is that Jim and Marianne are likely to be seen as 'undeserving' compared with respectable citizens like Esther Hurdle, and may be at the bottom of any priority list.

Who provides housing for community care?

Housing associations

Housing associations are non-profit-distributing organisations run by voluntary committees. Some cater for general needs, others are more specialist. They are financed by housing association grants (HAGs) and special needs management allowances (SNMAs).

Local authorities

Local authorities own a decreasing amount of council housing for the general population and also provide sheltered accommodation – in 1996 16 per cent of total local authority housing stock. Some older sheltered housing is hard to let because accommodation with shared facilities, such as bathrooms, is unpopular with older people used to the comforts of their own homes.

NHS

The NHS has built residential units for patients being transferred from long-stay hospitals, especially disabled people, and people with long-term mental health problems.

In the light of this discussion of one important aspect of provision, we can say with some certainty that matching Jim and Marianne's needs to the available resources will be a major challenge to any care manager. Their own preferences are likely to come well down the list.

Community responses

Contrasting communities

As far as people like Jim and Marianne are concerned, a care manager is going to be aware of likely community responses to any decision to house former or continuing drug users in residential areas, as well as accusations that such people are less deserving than others needing care. Implicitly, if not explicitly, practitioners making arrangements for 'difficult' clients, such as drug users, are expected to take into account the well-being and rights of the community at large, as well as that of the individuals. You can see from the quotations given here that some are seen as more deserving of help than others:

> *Neighbours slam family from hell.*
>
> (Beds on Sunday, *27 April 1997*)
>
> *Putting girls into Council flats and providing tax payer funded childcare is a policy from hell.*
>
> (Stephen Green, Chairman, Conservative Family Campaign, 1993)
>
> *I've got a little list of young ladies who get pregnant just to jump the housing list.*
>
> (Peter Lilley, then Social Services Secretary, October 1992)

Emotional adjustment

Becoming a new user of community care services, whoever you are, can be stressful. Remember what Marianne said just before leaving hospital: 'Look at me now. What a way to live. I wouldn't do it to a dog.' There will be a period of emotional adjustment to new roles, identities and physical or mental limitations. Here is what Baldock and Ungerson wrote about the responses of the people they interviewed to their new situations a few months after leaving hospital:

> *These later phases of emotional distress were a direct consequence of what we have called the 'unscripted nature of social dependency' ... They had returned home to find the legitimate normality of their lives undermined by their new disabilities ... they lead to changed relationships with other people, particularly close kin, and they lead to a new and often less confident and less powerful sense of identity ... Professionals necessarily focus primarily on tackling the more objective difficulties and know well the stubborn objections of people who, for example, refuse to be seen in a wheelchair, to accept moving the bed downstairs ... the objections are not to the practicality ... of the solutions but rather to the disturbance to the known and scripted routines of daily life, and the uncertainty about the appropriate new forms of behaviour and relationship.*
>
> (Baldock and Ungerson, 1994, p. 46)

If we think of the position of newcomers to community care in terms of learning new scripts to accompany their unwonted position of dependency, it becomes easier to understand why even copious quantities of written and verbal information and the best assessments of practical needs may not be enough to ease the transition.

3.4 Overcoming the barriers?

The chances of overcoming the barriers I have identified appear to be small. In Section 5 of this unit we spend more time on different strategies for change. But within the context of the community care system, can anything be done to improve practice? Some of the issues we have explored, such as shortage of resources, rules about residence and the response of the wider community, are not within an individual's power to change substantially. But some of the issues I have highlighted – provision of accessible information, awareness that an assessment is going on, and emotional responses – can be addressed by individual care managers. They will need to bear in mind that:

- most people will need a good deal of help if they are to be effective users of community care services

- assessments may be an everyday experience for workers – but they are often quite a new experience for service users

- people need information, but information alone is not enough

- relationships must take into account people's need for adjustment to new roles and relationships as well as their objective material needs

- if assessment is to be effective in meeting changing needs, then it has to be an ongoing process.

It is not only care managers who will have the opportunity to make use of the insights this section offers. All kinds of workers or volunteers come into contact with new users of community care, and an awareness of the issues involved as people take on new roles will help to improve practice.

This view offers practitioners a way of looking at the world that does not only blame resource constraints, but looks beyond those to consider how, even in a world where resources are not infinite (and they never are or will be), those who work in care services might do better if they have a little more understanding of the feelings and the difficulties of adjustment that new service users experience.

Key points

- Enabling users of services and their families to make choices was an aim of the community care reforms.

- Under the NHS and Community Care Act 1990, up until very recently, social services departments had a duty to publish an annually updated community care plan, one of whose purposes is to inform users of the range of services in their area. These documents are to be replaced by a range of others, which will outline the entitlements that users of community care can expect.

- Community care assessments have the potential to play a key role in offering choice to users of community care services. However, there are many barriers to the exercise of choice. Help from practitioners to new users needs to incorporate a recognition that people need support in understanding their entitlements and adjusting to new situations. Assessment needs to be seen as an ongoing process.

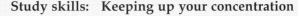

Study skills: Keeping up your concentration

Do you feel you are settling into a rhythm of studying now? Are you managing to avoid the kind of bitty, distracted sessions you read about in the case of Zahra, on pages 14 and 15 of *The Good Study Guide*? Have you got over the urge to make a cup of tea as soon as you have seated yourself, or to tidy your shelves? Of course, there are reasons why it is so easy to be distracted when you study – look back quickly at the box on page 39 of *The Good Study Guide*. You need to understand what helps you concentrate.

Think back over your best sessions of study. When have you concentrated particularly well? Was it when you:

- had set yourself a clear target?

- switched regularly from one task to another?

- made a point of scanning ahead so that you knew what you were reading about?

- were fresh from a nap?

- were really interested in the topic?

Or did other things keep you focused? You are the best person to work out what helps you concentrate. You need to take the time to try out different approaches and then reflect on what has been effective. But talking to other students can also be very helpful. When you hear about other people's study habits you begin to recognise where your own are distinctive. And sometimes you hear yourself explaining points about your ways of studying that you had never quite realised before. The more insight you have into your own motivation, capabilities and habits of thought, the better you can plan to play to your strengths. Don't feel you have to study according to some universal formula. There isn't one. Make up your own.

Section 4
Choice of services in the mixed economy of care

In Section 3 we considered how far users of services can exercise choice over their community care packages. If there is to be choice, then there has to be a variety of services to choose from for any particular need. This is what is meant by the 'mixed economy of care'. In this section we take a close look at issues for users in gaining access to services in a mixed economy.

4.1 Mapping the mixed economy

We discussed in Unit 3 how the community care reforms of 1990 introduced the idea of a mixed economy of care, with services provided from a number of different sources and purchased on behalf of the user by a care manager. The intention was to move from monopoly suppliers, where services were available only from state services, to a system that utilised the private, voluntary and informal sectors. It meant opening up the possibility that contributions could be made from 'the community' too. It would obviously be an over-simplification to suggest that before 1990 all services were supplied by the statutory sector of health and social services. You need only think of individuals, such as childminders, or long-established voluntary organisations, such as the Red Cross, the NSPCC and Barnardos, to realise that there has always been a variety of providers of social care. But, since the reforms, the variety of providers has increased dramatically, and the role of social services in providing services has correspondingly reduced. The example in the box shows how one local authority diversified provision.

The mixed economy in Wandsworth

In 1997 the London Borough of Wandsworth had gone further than most in creating a mixed economy of care.

- Its six children's homes were run by Shaftesbury Homes and Arethusa, a voluntary organisation.

- Its old people's homes were run by housing associations and a private sector health care company.

- Its day care centres and luncheon clubs were run by local voluntary groups.

- Its meals on wheels were run by a private contractor.

- Its home care services were run by the council, which had won the contract in a tendering competition against other providers.

(Adapted from Daniels, 1997, p. 4)

However, the more providers of services there are, the more sophisticated people have to be if they are to make use of increased choice.

To illustrate the complexities of accessing the mixed economy we turn to Baldock and Ungerson, whose study I cited in Section 3. They interviewed 32 stroke victims who were new to community care services in East Kent in the early days of the community care reforms (1992–4). They found that in the early months of being users people had used a huge range of helping services. They grouped sources of help into five categories:

- kin (or relatives)
- privately purchased
- voluntary
- neighbours
- public sector.

I shall take just one of these categories, privately purchased care, to examine in detail. The box below summarises Baldock and Ungerson's findings on the sources of help their respondents made use of in the private sector.

Privately purchased care

1   Medical services, e.g. private hospital care*, private nursing home care*

2   Paramedical services:

    (a)   physiotherapy*

    (b)   chiropody*

    (c)   speech therapy*

3   Complementary therapies, e.g. homeopathy, osteopathy

4   Aids and adaptations:

    (a)   major aids, e.g. hoists, wheelchairs, stairlifts, lifts*

    (b)   minor aids, e.g. ramps, handrails*

    (c)   internal reorganisation of house, e.g. installation of shower/bath/lavatory

> (d)   alarm system*
>
> (e)   entry phone*
>
> 5   Private purchase of new accommodation suited to dependence
>
> 6   Use of private car to access care or make it more palatable
>
> 7   Social care:
>
> (a)   private residential care: (1) permanent*, (2) respite*
>
> (b)   private day care*
>
> (c)   private home care, including personal care, on periodic basis*
>
> (d)   private domestic help, on periodic basis
>
> (e)   gardener, on periodic basis
>
> (f)   live-in housekeeper/companion.
>
> * Forms of care for which there are direct substitutes available free or heavily subsidised in the pubic sector, but which are also in short supply in the public sector (at least in East Kent)
>
> *(Adapted from Baldock and Ungerson, 1994, p. 33)*

You can see from the box that the services range from the sorts of thing almost anyone might purchase – a car, the services of a builder, a gardener, a new home – to quite specialised services, which they might need help from professionals or specialist information sources to access. This is especially the case for the medical services mentioned.

The information in the box suggests that people with money were at an advantage over people who were poor in making use of the private sector. Baldock and Ungerson's respondents identified possession of a car as being the single most important factor that promoted access and choice. If they had the use of a car, the stroke victims could use the services available to them selectively.

> *Mr. T, 87, decided to drive Mrs. T, 86, to the Day Hospital at times that would allow her to just use the parts of the service she wanted:*
>
> *Mr. T: They wanted to take her in the ambulance.*
>
> *Mrs. T: It's eight o'clock or something in the morning, and seven in the evening home!*
>
> *Mr. T: So I used to take her in every Wednesday morning about 10 o'clock, go off to Ashford Market, and then pick her up again on the way home.*
>
> *Mrs. T: It saved you all that terrible waiting in the afternoon for the ambulance. We'd done all the physiotherapy and the speech therapy. In the afternoons they used to make us do little things like tripping (sic) our hands up and down, you know, all very good, but everybody's thinking 'I've got things I could be doing at home'.*
>
> *(Baldock and Ungerson, 1994, p. 32)*

But there were other factors that enabled people to make use of sources of help, or hindered them. You'll see in the box that there are asterisks by the sorts of services that were also provided in the public sector.

Some of Baldock and Ungerson's respondents feared that if they used these services it would prejudice their chances of getting the heavily subsidised or free help from the public sector if it became available. In Mr and Mrs E's view, the fact that they had employed a physiotherapist privately had put them at the back of the queue for the NHS-supplied service, and they believed it may have been seen as an implicit criticism of the NHS service (p. 29).

A further point to note from the information in the box is that only a minority of the private services listed here were things a care manager might be expected to suggest. Much of the research had been done by the users themselves, or their relatives, utilising their existing knowledge of local services, advice from friends, or directories such as Yellow Pages. People like Jim and Marianne, who are not members of settled communities, will be disadvantaged.

Baldock and Ungerson's study shows that a 'mixed economy' existed in East Kent in the early 1990s, with services available from a wide array of providers. In that sense it was a success story for the mixed economy. But not everyone was successful in gaining access to the range of choice on offer.

We go on to examine possible reasons for this.

4.2 Explaining user behaviour

In Unit 4 we discussed the idea that people follow the equivalent of scripts to enable them to play the wide variety of roles expected in daily life. We used the example of interactions between doctor and patient to show how powerful such scripts are in determining the way people present themselves, who asks the questions, and what sort of limits there are on the roles that can be adopted in such familiar situations. In Section 2 of this unit I referred to these doctor–patient interactions again. Indeed, Jim's account of the dusty reception they got at the hands of one or two primary care teams could be seen as a failure on their parts to play the right sort of patient role, through being scruffy or dirty, or arriving at the wrong time for surgery, or making inappropriate demands of the person they were speaking to.

Baldock and Ungerson's research suggested that a way of understanding some of the problems experienced by users of community care services is that they are suddenly being required to play new roles to new scripts, and no one has told them the lines. In Section 3 I quoted their findings that new users have a considerable emotional adjustment to make when they find themselves in the unwonted position of being 'dependent'. Baldock and Ungerson suggest that the change to a mixed economy can exacerbate people's difficulties of adjustment. They argue that:

• People for the most part did not expect care services to be obtained on the open market; they were used to being told what to do.

• This sort of mixed economy was unlike the retail market of shops and mail order. In the mixed economy of care some services were free, some were charged for, some could be bought on the open market, some not, and some were available from a variety of sources.

To assist in understanding people's behaviour they created a model which places users of community care into four ideal types. You will find it described in Chapter 29 of the Reader.

Activity 8 Describing the model

Allow about 30 minutes  Read Chapter 29 of the Reader, 'Becoming consumers of community care'. Then make your own notes on the four types of user described.

Comment You'll see that the model sets up four types of user:

Consumers – who expect nothing from the state and set out to arrange care by buying it, just as they might buy a new car, or any other kind of consumer goods. They believe that using the market in this way gives them more control and autonomy than using state services, even if they are free.

Privatists – who focus their lives on their homes, and who find dependence hard to adjust to because it often means asking for help. The market does not meet all their needs, and they tend to become isolated.

Welfarists – who expect and demand their rights to welfare services as citizens, and have the know-how and energy to get the best out of the public and voluntary services.

Clientists – who rather passively accept what they are offered, without either demanding more or expecting that the services will respond to their needs in anything but a rigid, prescribed way.

Like all models, this is a representation of reality – no one fell exactly into any one category. Nevertheless, it can be a helpful way to think about the range of scripts available to new users.

Activity 9 Applying the model

Allow about 20 minutes Using what you have learnt from Chapter 29 of the Reader, answer the following questions:

(a)   Jim and Marianne are, as I have noted, unlike the people interviewed by Baldock and Ungerson. Which, if any, of the four categories do you think best represents their likely script, and why?

(b)   Where in the model would you place:

  •   the Durrants (Block 1)

  •   the Brights (Block 2)

  •   the arguments in favour of independent living (Unit 3)?

Comment   (a)   Judging from what has been said about Jim and Marianne in this unit so far, it seems likely they will adopt either the welfarist or the clientist scripts. They do not have the money to be privatists, and their history of being consumers is weak. Since they already have some know-how from earlier in their lives, for example in locating sympathetic GPs, they might have the energy and inside knowledge to actively pursue their entitlements (welfarism); but, as Marianne said, when they are not feeling too good about themselves, the sort of passive acceptance of what is offered that characterises clientism seems likely. An alternative is that they will drop out of the system and return to the streets – which is perhaps a form of self-defeating privatism.

(b)   The Durrants fit most easily into the clientist script. They do not appear to have the knowledge or resources to fight effectively for flexible services to meet their needs, and lack of cash means they cannot utilise the private sector, except via the care manager.

Mrs Bright's energetic pursuit of extra services when she needs them places her more in a welfarist script.

The arguments in favour of independent living seem to fall between welfarism (in the sense of actively pursuing entitlements using rights-based arguments) and consumerism (arranging care on the open market).

Models, as Baldock and Ungerson say in the Reader, are only a crude method of representing the different ways people respond to new situations. The model they presented was drawn from only one group in one area of the country. A similar project investigating a different group – say drug users – or in a different part of the UK might throw up different lists and different models. But models *are* useful in helping to make sense of complex situations.

4.3 From welfare state to mixed economy

I have suggested that, as the philosophy of care provision moved from the expectations set up by the post-1945 welfare state, of care from cradle to grave, to a system in which 'market', 'consumer choice', 'competition' and 'mixed economy' were the watchwords, if users were to be 'successful' they had to adapt their behaviour to make the best use of the new environment. Baldock and Ungerson's research shows that some people (consumers and welfarists) – those with most private resources, confidence and knowledge – can make good use of the opportunities offered in a mixed economy. But those who are impoverished, have few community networks, are very frail or confused, or who are perceived as 'difficult', appear to find it hard to take advantage of the opportunities for choice, and may have been better served by the promises of universal equitable care for all which characterised the mid-twentieth-century welfare state.

You have seen throughout this unit that 'difficult' or 'disadvantaged' people experience considerable barriers in gaining access to health and social care services in the community, and that even when they do access such services, their opportunities to make choices are limited. In the final section of this unit we explore some strategies that have been advocated to promote access to services designed to benefit everyone, but especially those most disadvantaged.

Key points

- The 'mixed economy' of care was ushered in by the NHS and Community Care Act 1990. It refers to the existence of a variety of providers of care and support – from private, voluntary and statutory services to neighbourhood networks and the support of relatives and friends – and is intended to promote choice by users of services.

- The mixed economy exists in some areas and for some services.

- Many users find it hard to access the benefits of the mixed economy partly because they are poor, frail or have little or no access to information and resources; and partly because the system is hard to comprehend.

Section 5
Strategies for change

This unit has spent some time exploring barriers to accessing a variety of community services – primary care, community care and housing. I have noted how far Jim and Marianne, and individuals like them who are seen as 'difficult', 'deviant' or just plain expensive, are disadvantaged when it comes to getting the services to which they are theoretically entitled, so much so that it may be tempting for them just to throw in the towel and give up. And you have seen that, although individual practitioners, GPs and care managers can have some impact, what they can achieve as individuals is limited both by resources and by the system.

Now it is time to consider what might be done to improve matters, what strategies for change exist and how far they might improve access for the likes of Jim and Marianne.

5.1 Charters: creating better consumers

In Section 2 reference was made to the rights of patients to GP services enshrined in the Patient's Charter, produced by the Department of Health. Charters can be seen as a way of making people better *consumers* by informing them of their rights. Some charters go further than the Patient's Charter.

The box below shows a charter of rights for drug users drawn up by SCODA (the Standing Conference on Drug Abuse). Unlike the Patient's Charter, this does not have the backing of central government. It can be seen as a set of aspirations, and has the advantage of being a users'-eye view of what people should have a right to demand.

Drug Users' Charter

Drug users have the right to:

- assessment of individual need within a specified number of days

- specialist services within a specified maximum waiting time

- respect for privacy, dignity and confidentiality

- a complaints procedure

- full information about treatment and informed involvement in making decisions about treatment

- a second opinion when referred to a consultant

- an individual care and treatment plan

- immediate access to treatment programmes on release from prison

- information about self help groups and drug user rights groups.

(Standing Conference on Drug Abuse, 1997, p. 3)

Activity 10   **The Drug Users' Charter**

Allow about 20 minutes   Using the Drug Users' Charter, make your own notes in answer to the following questions:

(a)   Who do you think might make use of such a charter – and when?

(b)   How do you think a service provider might react if presented with such a charter?

Comment   (a)   Inevitably, I thought of Jim and Marianne as likely users of such a charter. They might use it when meeting a GP who was resistant to accepting them, or maybe when they wanted a particular treatment or course of action which was being denied.

(b)   I found it hard to think of a practitioner reacting positively, and imagined many viewing such an action as a condemnation of the treatment that was being offered.

On reflection, I could see the charter as useful to have as a last resort, if it was impossible to get satisfaction by any other means.

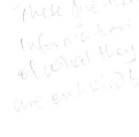

Charters do give users an idea of their rights but, as the activity shows, it is difficult to see how they can be used routinely. The rights are often couched in general terms, and hard to translate into action. Charters do not mean that there are more resources, just that some people (perhaps the sorts who are successful welfarists) may be better able to access what there is. As a strategy for change, unless ways can be found of providing the kinds of service drug users need and persuading agencies that they should adopt these as aspirations, charters have limited use.

5.2 Advocacy

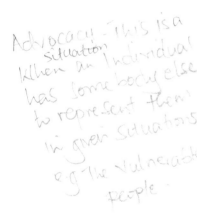

What is advocacy? An advocate is defined by Ken Simons as an 'unconditional ally for an individual who is vulnerable; someone to be on the side of their partner' (Simons, 1993, p. 14). The principles of advocacy may be applicable to anyone whose rights and wishes are ignored or overruled. There are numerous types of advocacy, ranging from agencies such as welfare rights organisations, to legal ombudsmen, professionals and workers whose role includes acting as an advocate for their patients or clients, to unpaid individuals who choose to take on the role.

There are many ways in which an advocate might work with Jim and Marianne.

- They might speak up for them at the doctors' surgery or at other agencies they will have to come into contact with, or encourage them to speak up for themselves.

- They might provide practical help with budgeting and sorting out domestic or housing matters.

- They might give advice and information on benefits, other agencies from which Jim and Marianne might get support, and so on.

- They might also offer friendship and help to re-establish a sense of self-worth for Jim and Marianne.

But who might be an advocate? Two types of advocacy are:

- *Paid professionals* acting as advocates as a part of the job.

- *Unpaid citizens* who take on the role as volunteers. Jim mentioned being an advocate himself when he worked briefly in the rehabilitation centre. At that time he describes going with other clients to visit their doctors' surgeries. Advocates can be family or friends, but the role can also be formalised through peer or citizen advocacy schemes. Such advocates enter into an independent, voluntary relationship with a person who needs someone to help them defend or exercise their rights, and to gain acceptance into the life of the community (Citizen Advocacy Information and Training, 1996).

There are advantages and disadvantages to both types of advocacy – paid professionals or workers acting for their patients/clients, and volunteers. Think this through by doing the next activity.

Activity 11 **Advocates for Jim and Marianne?**

Allow about 10 minutes   Answer the following questions briefly.

(a) If Jim and Marianne's GP decided to act as an advocate for them, what might he be able to offer? What factors might limit his effectiveness as an advocate? (It will help if you consider the issues raised in the discussion of Chapter 5 in the Reader, in Section 1.)

(b) If you were a trained volunteer citizen advocate, what might you be able to offer? What might limit your effectiveness?

Comment   (a) As a local health professional a GP could offer a knowledge of what might be available, and might be able to exert pressure to ensure that Jim and Marianne were accepted into a suitable service. But his professional code of conduct might mean he was obliged to report on any illegal activities. If they had had children he might not have been able to act as their unconditional ally. In addition, he might need to consider the likely reactions of colleagues and others if he seemed to be favouring one couple over other patients. He would also need to be prepared to be self-critical, and recognise that he may be part of the problem!

(b) Most course testers observed that as a citizen advocate they would have fewer conflicts of role to consider than a paid professional acting as an advocate. One commented:

'At least I could be quite single-minded, and would not need to worry about other patients.'

However, others sounded a note of caution:

'I'm not sure I'd want to be involved if it meant turning a blind eye to illegal activities like dealing in drugs.'

'Where do you start? At least a worker knows the system. I'd be starting from scratch.'

'I'd be wondering if I wanted to take on an open-ended commitment. I might not even like them.'

'How would I find them when I wanted to speak to them? They haven't even got a phone number.'

In advocacy there is a balance to consider between independence and absence of role conflict (most likely to be found in volunteers) and the advantages of local know-how, which are most likely to lie with community-based workers.

Both strategies, charters and advocacy, appear to have the potential to help Marianne and Jim to some extent. We have seen that neither strategy is without its problems, but taken together there is hope for change. Without an advocate or ally, they may not be successful in putting their charter rights into operation. But the sort of statement of rights or aspirations that charters provide can be a starting point for an advocate who might volunteer to work with Jim and Marianne.

One criticism that can be levelled at such individualistic strategies is that they may advantage some people – make them into more successful consumers – but when resources are limited others who do not have these advantages may lose out.

The next two strategies for change we examine aim at the community at large, rather than at particular individuals.

5.3 Community outreach

'Outreach' is the term used to describe activities that seek to reach people who are not making use of services they need. You have seen that homeless people and drug users who want treatment often find it hard to come by health and care services. Judgemental attitudes combined with competition for limited resources mean that many are deterred, despite the rights they have under the Patient's Charter. The consequences can be dire for the individual, and costly for health and care services when individuals become as ill as were Jim and Marianne when they entered hospital. A strategy to bridge the gap is community outreach.

In a rural area of north-east Essex drug users themselves were recruited and trained as outreach volunteers. They were given the task of contacting drug users and assisting them in practices to reduce harm, such as using sterile syringes, advising on drug services locally and providing information on safer sex. Building on existing networks, the drug user volunteers made a considerable impact. They knew where drug users met, and were able to incorporate their work as volunteers in their daily lives. Results from a survey of the scheme (Boulton and Walling, 1993, p. 15) show that:

- 46 of 66 respondents had heard of the scheme

- 34 (over 50 per cent) were in regular contact with a volunteer

- 23 of those 34 who were in contact with a volunteer were not in contact with any other drug service

- the informal syringe exchange service established by volunteers had made an impact – there was less sharing of syringes

- the volunteers themselves experienced increased self-esteem and social standing.

The authors of the report on the north-east Essex scheme believe that the use of drug users as volunteers brought considerable benefits. However, monitoring the scheme proved impossible because, as they write:

> *Volunteers do not want to keep records or report to someone on what they do ... Volunteers who were being most successful in drugs outreach were the ones most opposed to monitoring.*
>
> (Boulton and Walling, 1993, p. 15)

Lack of monitoring means that drug use is still poorly documented or understood, and it is hard to make a strong case for more funding or better services. The illegality of drug use means that arguing for more services is dubious anyway.

Community outreach is a strategy that is applicable to groups other than drug users. Homeless people are another group that is hard to reach, as are some members of Minority Ethnic groups who may be unaware of the sorts of service they can expect, or be deterred by the expectation that they will meet prejudice, or be offered services that simply do not meet their needs.

One drawback is that successful outreach may well stimulate a demand for services which are non-existent or already at full stretch. If the north-east Essex scheme had prompted drug users to come forward for rehabilitation, could the existing services have responded? Giles Woolford's family spent a year badgering for a place in a detoxification centre when he decided he wanted to break the hold heroin had over him. In the end he got two weeks in hospital – not enough to prevent his sliding back into addiction within a month (Bosely, 1997, p. 2). Like charters and advocacy, outreach is a strategy that can make a difference, but without more and better services, the impact will be limited.

5.4 Experimental health centres

Strategies that can make services to be more accessible by vulnerable people
(1) community outreach
(2) Advocacy
(3) patient charters

We have looked at making services more accessible through various strategies – charters, advocacy, community outreach. It is probably unrealistic to expect that drug addicts, perceived to be among the least deserving of the thousands of people in competition for scarce resources, should ever expect to have as much as they may need to break them of their addiction, and support them in the difficult adjustment to life after drugs. An alternative strategy is to create services that have a broad vision of serving the health of the whole community.

The Peckham Experiment

You might like to write this on to the wallchart

Within primary care, developments are taking place that are evidence of changed ways of thinking about health and that acknowledge the influence of social, economic and environmental factors in the health of individual people and the communities in which they live. Many of these new initiatives have adopted the thinking behind the 'Peckham Experiment'. In 1926, the Peckham Experiment was initiated, based on an innovative health centre which would provide a range of social, recreational and fitness activities for local people. The aim was to foster 'positive health' and 'to create the right conditions for the emergence of health rather than just the treatment of disease'. The Pioneer Health Centre opened in 1935 and included a swimming pool, gym, badminton courts, games rooms, playground, nursery, cafeteria and dance hall. The biologists who established the project believed that, given the opportunity, individuals and families would choose healthy options. Their core principles included:

- *an orientation towards health, interpreted in a broad, holistic way*

- *member participation and self determination*

- *multi-generational membership*

- *a range of opportunities/integrated activities.*

(Gaskin and Vincent, 1996a, p. 14)

The Peckham Experiment

Below is a description of what the Peckham Experiment offered to local people:

> *Here was an environment for the chance meeting; but also, and more important, for continual and repeated meetings, and so for acquaintanceship, companionship and developing friendships ... Everything taking place there was carried on by people who, belonging to the locality and continuously using the Centre, came to be known personally to each other through sharing in some of the many facilities of the Centre life; or through the day to day doings of their children; or merely known by sight as members participating in a common experience.*
>
> *(Pioneer Health Centre, 1971, p. 4)*

More recent innovations have followed many of these principles (Scott-Samuel, 1990) and a recent report evaluating the effectiveness of co-operative, socially based, primary care initiatives concludes:

> *Evidence suggests that we are at a landmark stage in the evolution of thinking about health. So many different elements appear to be coming together and culminating in a qualitative shift in the culture of health care delivery and health promotion. This challenges our social and political system to respond with creative and effective new forms. On the evidence so far, the models of community well-being centres and co-operative structures offer exciting new ways of realising the potential of people and communities to improve the overall health of the nation as we move into the 21st Century.*
>
> *(Gaskin and Vincent, 1996b, p. 76)*

How far such approaches might embrace the issues that confront Jim and Marianne is doubtful. Setting aside the illegal nature of their habit, which such a place is unlikely to countenance, the Peckham Centre was locality based – and Jim and Marianne have little to connect them to where they happen to live. It is indeed hard to imagine 'the community' embracing transient outcasts like them. Or could *they* change, given the opportunity to enjoy a healthier lifestyle?

5.5 Reviewing strategies for change

The strategies to improve access to services discussed in this section are wide-ranging, sometimes idealistic, sometimes exciting. They all offer potential. None can be seen as a straightforward blueprint for addressing the problems faced by Jim and Marianne, our reference point so far, but they are well worth consideration when thinking about the broad topic of this unit, access to health and social care.

Conclusion

In this unit you have been considering questions of access to community services. The nature of community as it is traditionally seen, as membership of a place with its accompanying networks and facilities, seems to exclude Jim and Marianne, and people like them. Jim and Marianne are people on the margins of community as it is usually conceived. They have very few of the attributes that confer membership of local communities – no home, no jobs, very little money, few local networks, little respect or self-confidence. Because most health and social care services assume that people who come to them will have some kind of community base, at the very least a home, they are at an immediate disadvantage when it comes to access. The disadvantages do not stop there. They face discrimination. Even if the individual practitioner is open-minded and welcoming, there lurk shadows – what will other people think, is there a threat to the welfare of others, what right do such people have to what is always a limited amount of resources, where is the line to be drawn between deserving and undeserving cases? In comparison with other user groups – disabled people and children in care, for example – drug users and homeless people command little public sympathy or support.

On the positive side, looking at the person behind the label can begin to redress the balance so that even the most disadvantaged and difficult people emerge as human beings whose problems, if they cannot be solved, can be understood and empathised with. Services at the very least aspire to be open to all who need them. And there is a range of strategies that can be explored as means to make the ideal of access for all more of a reality.

What general lessons can be learnt about access to community services from your study in this unit? Three points stand out.

1   If the intention is to maximise access it is not enough to place a service geographically within a community and publicise its existence. It is not even enough to undertake an individual needs assessment.

2   Services need to be fitted to people, rather than people being expected to fit in with services. They need to adapt to different kinds of user and potential user, and remain alert to who is left out.

3   Many mainstream services assume that users will have a home and be part of a geographical community. Some people have neither.

If you have time, make your own links from the conclusion to this unit to the core questions now, just to make sure you have grasped the main ideas. The core questions were:

•   What barriers are there to access to community health and care services?

•   To what extent can people exercise choice in the services they access?

•   What strategies exist to promote access to services for people who are disadvantaged?

Services should be adaptable to various people

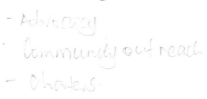
– Advocacy
– Community outreach
– Charters

Study skills: Granting yourself the time

I talked earlier about the little distractions that can so easily
disturb your studies. But what about more urgent distractions –
worries about untouched housework, pressures at work, getting
the WC repaired, keeping the children from self-destruction? Are
you feeling guilty right now about what you have failed to achieve
outside your studies, as well as your shortcomings within the
course? Is this whole study thing a bad idea?

How can you balance all the demands from outside K100 against
your own need for personal development through study? You
need to think about the priorities in your life. Some things just
won't get done – or will not be done as thoroughly as before you
were studying. But are you giving more time to K100 than you can
really afford? Or are there other things you need to drop, to take
some of the pressure off? Do you need to talk to family or friends
to explain the demands on your time?

Now that you have two months' experience of K100 you need to
be looking for a balance in your life as an independent student.
You need to weigh up what is important so that you can grant
yourself a suitable amount of study time. The worst of all worlds
is to find yourself wasting hard-won study time while worrying
about what you are not doing elsewhere.

References

Association of Community Health Councils for England and Wales (1994) *Patients' Rights*, Association of Community Health Councils for England and Wales, London.

Baldock, J. and Ungerson, C. (1994) *Becoming Consumers of Community Care*, Joseph Rowntree Foundation, York.

Boulton, K. and Walling, A. (1993) 'User to user', *Druglink*, July/August, pp. 14–15.

Bosely, S. (1997) 'When love isn't enough', *Guardian*, 21 April.

Citizen Advocacy Information and Training (1996) *CAIT Information*, CAIT, London.

Daniels, A. (1997) '"No essential reason" to insist on in-house services', *Guardian*, 13 March, p. 4.

Davies, A. and Huxley, P. (1997) 'Survey of general practitioners' opinions on treatment of opiate users', *British Medical Journal*, Vol. 314, 19 April, pp. 1173–4.

Department of Health (1989a) *An Introduction to the Children Act 1989*, HMSO, London.

Department of Health (1989b) *Caring for People*, Cm 849, HMSO, London.

Department of Health (1996) *Primary Care: Delivering the future*, Cm 3511, HMSO, London.

Department of Health (2001a) *Your Guide to the NHS*, Department of Health, London, www.nhs.uk/nhsguide/home.htm [accessed 27.5.02].

Department of Health (2001b) *Involving Patients and the Public in Healthcare: A discussion document*, Department of Health, London, www.doh.gov.uk/involvingpatients [accessed 27.5.02].

Department of Health (2001c) *Involving Patients and the Public in Healthcare: Response to the listening exercise*, Department of Health, London, www.doh.gov.uk/involvingpatients [accessed 27.5.02].

Department of Health (2002) *Patient Advice and Liaison Services*, www.doh.gov.uk/patientadviceandliaisonservices/index.htm [accessed 27.5.02].

Franks, P., Clancy, C. and Nutting, P. (1992) 'Gatekeeping revisited – protecting patients from overtreatment', *New England Journal of Medicine*, Vol. 327, pp. 424–9.

Gaskin, K. and Vincent, J. (1996a) 'Peckham principles and co-operation in community well-being schemes', *Purchasing in Practice*, Vol. 10, pp. 14–15.

Gaskin, K. and Vincent, J. (1996b) *Co-operating for Health: The potential of the co-operative movement and community well-being centres to health of the nation activities*, Centre for Research in Social Policy, Loughborough University, Loughborough.

Greenwood, J. (1992) 'Persuading general practitioners to prescribe – good husbandry or a recipe for chaos?' *British Journal of Addiction*, Vol. 87, pp. 567–74, http://www.doh.gov.uk/patientadviceandliaisonservices/index.htm [accessed 27.5.02]

Hadley, R. and Clough, R. (1996) *Care in Chaos*, Cassell, London.

Kidd, B. and Stark, C. (1995) *Management of Violence and Aggression in Health Care*, Gaskell/Royal College of Psychiatrists, London.

Leaver, E.J., Elford, J., Morris, J.K. and Cohen, J. (1992) 'Use of general practice by intravenous heroin users on a methadone programme', *British Journal of General Practice*, Vol. 42, pp. 465–8.

McKeganey, N. (1988) 'Shadowland: general practitioners and the treatment of opiate abusing patients', *British Journal of Addiction*, Vol. 83, pp. 373–86.

North, C., Moore, H. and Owens, C. (1996) *Go Home and Rest?*, Shelter, London.

Pioneer Health Centre (1971) *The Peckham Experiment*, Pioneer Health Centre, London.

Roberts, G. (1996) 'Empowerment and community care: some of the legal issues', in Ramcharan, P., Roberts, G., Grant, G. and Borland, J. (eds) *Empowerment in Everyday Life: Learning disability*, Jessica Kingsley, London.

Scott-Samuel, A. (ed.) (1990) *Total Participation, Total Health; Re-inventing the Peckham Health Centre for the 1990s*, Scottish Academic Press, Edinburgh.

Simons, K. (1993) *Citizen Advocacy: The inside view*, Norah Fry Research Centre, Bristol.

Social Services Inspectorate/Scottish Social Work Group (1991) *Care Management and Assessment: Manager's guide*, HMSO, London.

Standing Conference on Drug Abuse (1997) *Getting Drug Users Involved*, SCODA, London.

Starfield, B. (1994) 'Is primary care essential?', *The Lancet*, Vol. 344, pp. 1129–33.

Starfield, B. (1995) 'Is strong primary care good for health outcomes?', lecture prepared for conference on the Future of Primary Care, Office of Health Economics, London, 13 September 1995.

Welsh, I. (1993) *Trainspotting*, Minerva, London.

Acknowledgements

Grateful acknowledgement is made to the following sources for permission to reproduce material in this unit:

Text

p. 33: Sheffield Community Care Services – Service Charter, Sheffield City Council, with permission; *pp. 42–43:* Baldock, J. and Ungerson, C. (1994) *Becoming Consumers of Community Care: Households Within the Mixed Economy of Welfare*, Joseph Rowntree Foundation.

Illustrations

p. 10: Christopher Jones; *pp. 18, 21:* Paul Schatzberger; *p. 36 (left):* R.G. Richards; *p. 42:* Courtesy of Ashbourne plc; *p. 53:* Hulton Getty.

Unit 11
Communities, Diversity and Care

Prepared for the course team by Lucy Rai (with acknowledgements to the previous unit by Martin Robb)

While you are working on Unit 11, you will need:

- Course Reader
- Offprints Book
- *The Good Study Guide*
- Audio Cassette 3, sides 1 and 2

Contents

Introduction

As you have seen in Unit 10, government policy focuses on 'the community' as both a source of support and a place where care takes place. However, living in the same place does not necessarily create a sense of community – many communities are made up of people who have very different backgrounds, experiences and beliefs. Unit 11 explores the diverse nature of modern communities and reflects on the way this diversity affects both the delivery of care and the experience of receiving care. In particular, it explores the implications for health and social care services of recognising the diversity of cultures in Britain today.

Meeting the care needs of the whole community is firstly about recognising cultural difference rather than assuming that everyone is the same. But it is also about recognising that some cultures and ways of life are given privileged status in our society and that for people whose beliefs and ways of life are not given such 'privileged status' this can have a serious impact on their experience of receiving services. Inadequate or inappropriate responses from care providers may stem from assumptions about a person's way of life based on their sexuality, age, physical or mental abilities, or gender. However, in this unit the focus is on race and ethnicity. Where care providers make assumptions based on the colour of a person's skin, their name or their nationality, they often misread both their culture and their needs.

The unit opens with a focus on the individual, a focus on *you*, if you like. Do you identify yourself with a community? How would you describe your own culture or your 'cultural identity'? What assumptions do you make about members of other cultures? In Section 2 you will begin to look at how the processes of stereotyping and prejudice operates in communities. In Section 3 I will present some examples of how racism can affect people working in the health service and also the lives of children living away from their parents, and again later when they leave local authority care as young adults. In Section 4 you will consider how racism operates at the institutional level and what implications this has for care practice. Finally, in Section 5 you will be introduced to some positive approaches to responding to racism. You will be able to apply your learning by recognising the skills required to develop anti-discriminatory and anti-racist practice as health or social care workers.

You may find that the material in this unit is quite challenging to your own beliefs and values. Some of the case study material is emotive and may evoke memories of personal experiences of discrimination or exclusion.

Core questions

- How do Black and Minority Ethnic people experience health and social care services in the UK?

- In what ways can stereotyping, prejudice, racism and discrimination affect the delivery of care at both an individual and institutional level?

- How can health and social care providers respond positively to meeting the needs of diverse communities?

Section 1
Belonging and being different

Being an 'individual' or being 'different' can be a valued characteristic. However, people also have a strong desire to feel that they have something in common with those around them. I might see myself as a woman, sharing common interests and experiences with other women, but I may also want to differentiate myself from particular women and could possibly feel strong associations with some men. At the same time I might think of myself as 'belonging' to more specific groups, say through being a political activist, by enjoying a particular type of music. Membership of such 'groups' is sometimes a matter of choice, as is the case with my hobbies or interests. On the other hand, I did not 'choose' my gender, my sexuality, my age, or whether I have a disability. Yet, whether chosen or not, membership of these groups contributes to how I see myself, to my sense of who I am. Such group membership, however, results in people being 'categorised' by society – by individual people and also by providers of services and policy makers. You may have come across politicians, journalists or people you know talking about 'The Disabled', 'The Gay Community' or 'The Older Generation' – do you think that by using these terms they mean that members of such groups are in some way 'the same' as each other? While a person may have a physical impairment, and so be 'disabled', this may not be the particular characteristic by which they wish to be defined. Assumptions about individuals' characteristics may lead to unjust or unequal treatment. This could be in the form of negative beliefs or attitudes but it may also result in members of such groups experiencing real disadvantage, for example in access to education, employment, housing and healthy lifestyles.

Diversity in society

Activity 1 What are your cultural roots?

Allow about 10 minutes

In a quick survey of colleagues in the office today, I asked for responses to the question 'Describe your cultural roots. How does your culture affect your daily life?' These are some of the answers I received:

> 'I'm a Brummie, but live in Leamington nowadays – a bit of a sell out to my working class roots! I was brought up on a council estate, football was our life as kids. Of course originally my family is from Ireland (my Dad was a Derry man) – catholic Irish of course - but we are not great churchgoers now. I still follow Irish music, though, and play the fiddle a bit. My brothers are the real ones for the music, though!'

> 'I see myself as Indian, sometimes as a British Asian. I'm a humanist in my beliefs, although I observe all the Hindu rituals that are required as a father and a husband. I call myself a Black activist because I see a commonality with people of colour from the developing world because of the experience of discrimination based on the colour of our skins. I am a middle-class professional,

although my family origins lie in coming from a village and being farmers.'

'I am a Scot. I was born in Glasgow and still have the accent even though I've not lived there for many years. My parents are Black British, they were born here but my grandparents came from East Africa originally. My partner is half Scots and half Iranian – so our kids are a real mixture! My partner and I are both Muslims – I would say that that is our culture as well as our religion.'

Spend 10 minutes thinking about how you would describe yourself.

Comment   You may have picked on a number of different ways to describe yourself, as my colleagues did, depending on what seems important to you and how you see yourself. You may have noted down things that you enjoy doing, such as your hobbies, or perhaps the beliefs or values that are important to you, such as your politics or religion.

Some aspects of who you are may be very individual to you, but some may be linked to your family and their history and ways of life. You may also feel that you share common ways of life with the people who live around you – your community. All of these contribute to your 'culture' – the important influences on how you lead your life.

1.1 Culture and ethnicity

Culture

We can think of 'culture', then, as beliefs, customs and ways of life passed on over generations, or adopted as a 'lifestyle' choice. Culture is important not only because it shapes how you act and think, but also because it gives you your sense of who you are – your identity. Other people can misinterpret your culture. The colour of your skin, the way you talk or your name are some of the 'hooks' on which others make judgements about who *they* think you are, but these judgements may not be accurate or helpful. Such judgements may also lead to assumptions that a 'culture' is something that only Black and Minority Ethnic people 'have', whereas in fact everybody has a culture.

Ethnicity

In the kind of society we live in today, we are almost certainly influenced by a wide range of cultural sources, such as the fashions and styles produced by international companies that make clothes, records, films and food products – as well as by local customs or family traditions. When we think of the broad cultural patterns linked to countries or to nationalities (as, for example, when we talk about the differences between Scottish, Welsh, Irish and English people, not to mention other European nations, such as French, Danish or German) we can add the word 'ethnic' and talk of an 'ethnic culture'. Avtar Brah suggests that ethnicities are maintained through:

> ...*a belief in common ancestry, claims to a shared history that gives shape to feelings of shared struggles and shared destinies, attachment to a homeland which may or may not coincide with the place of residence, and a sense of belonging to a group with a shared language, religion, social customs and traditions.*

(Brah, 1993, p. 15)

In the past the term 'ethnic' has tended to be associated with things that are 'different' or 'unfamiliar'. So 'white British' people spoke of 'ethnic food', 'ethnic dancing' or 'ethnic art', meaning 'not white British'. But clearly this is a lopsided view. We are all influenced by our cultural roots. Everybody has culture and 'ethnicity'. So, although the term 'ethnic' is often associated with 'minority', it ought to be just as appropriate to talk of 'ethnicities' within those sections of the population not thought of as 'minorities'.

On the other hand, this unit is about the experiences within the UK care services of members of Minority Ethnic groups, and because there are very proper sensitivities about the language used to refer to these groups, it is important to choose the right words.

Terminology Box 1

As you saw in Unit 1, when a 'label' is put on people with a particular physical impairment or mental illness, the meaning tends to change over time and become offensive. Similarly, when labels are attached to ethnic groups the meanings tend to shift, influencing what people view as being acceptable or offensive. For example, although words such as 'golliwog', 'sambo' and 'coloured' were common a few decades ago, they have almost disappeared as people now regard them as offensive. Meanwhile, Minority Ethnic groups have become organised and have developed their own terms to identify themselves (or in some cases reclaimed older terms).

One example is the use of the word Black, which was reclaimed by African Americans in the 1960s as something to be proud off. Since then, Black has been widely used as an umbrella term which acknowledges the common experience of racism that all non-white people have faced and continue to face (Lambeth Social Services Committee, 1981). However there are differences of opinion on the acceptable use of the term. Some people from Asia have objected to being described as 'Black', and more recently a group of Africans in Scotland have led a campaign against its use. As a result, other phrases have come into use such as 'people of colour' and 'minority ethnic'. The Scottish Executive has adopted 'minority ethnic' as its standard term.

In this unit I use the phrase 'Black and Minority Ethnic' unless I am referring to a person of a specific heritage.

(The simplest and most appropriate approach is to ask whoever you are working with how they wish to be identified.)

Although in this unit you will be exploring the shared experiences of members of Black and Minority Ethnic groups within the care services, it is of course important to emphasise that people are individuals as well as members of groups. Not only are there enormous differences between individual members of any ethnic group, but for some people their ethnic identity and culture is more important than it is for others. We may all be influenced by the groups we belong to and their cultural traditions, but we are not all influenced to the same extent and in the same way.

1.2 Acknowledging difference

You are going to begin exploring the nature of cultural differences by meeting two members of a Minority Ethnic group. Many of the people you will meet in this unit are members of non-white ethnic groups, but since it would be misleading to give the impression of equating minority status with skin colour, the first two women you meet are members of a white Minority Ethnic group – Gypsy Travellers.

Activity 2   **Looking for evidence of cultural difference**

Allow about 10 minutes

For this activity listen to Audio Cassette 3, section 1. In this excerpt Kathleen and Rita talk about their feelings about their culture and the way in which they think other people interpret it.

As you listen, note down any examples of cultural practices that seem different or similar to your own. If you have the opportunity, share your answers with someone who you see as belonging to a different cultural group. You might also think about whether you can see any positive benefits in the practices described.

Comments   As you listened to Rita and Kathleen you will have responded from the perspective of your own cultural background. Some of the practices described may have seemed similar to your family traditions, but some may have seemed quite different.

- Rita and Kathleen talked about needing to keep a very tidy and well organised home. This may at first not seem particularly 'cultural', but the way individuals organise their homes is very likely to be influenced by the way they were brought up.

- Rita and Kathleen also describe 'churching', the practice of women staying in bed for the first 10 days after childbirth. This is a time when most women rest, and they are not permitted to prepare food. This practice will be familiar to some of you, for example those of you who are familiar with Hindu birth practices. While it may seem to restrict women's lives, it is also a practice which ensures that new mothers are able to rest and spend quiet time with their babies, while depending on the practical support of their families.

It is clear as you listen to Rita and Kathleen that the things they do in their daily lives are very normal to them. Their routines make sense as part of the whole way they look at life – their beliefs, what is important to them, and what seems right.

As in most modern societies, in Britain there is a great diversity of ways of life. Yet, like Rita and Kathleen, we all live within worlds that seem 'normal' and 'natural' to us. We feel we have good reasons for doing things the way we do, and tend to be unaware of just how many other well reasoned ways of doing things there are in society around us – the many other 'normalities' within which people live their lives. Does this matter? As long as you are comfortable within your own way of life, is that not enough? Not if you are a carer. Carers cross the boundaries between their own lives and the lives of those they provide care for, and they must be aware of cultural difference. If they are going to contribute to people's well-being, they must be able to understand the way in which they themselves see the world and what is important to them. They must also be ready to value other people's ways of life. In short, they must be ready to recognise and to acknowledge difference and to value cultural diversity.

Gypsy Travellers

Key points

- The way we see ourselves is a complex mixture of the groups we feel we 'belong' to.

- The lives of all of us are rooted in 'culture' and 'ethnicity'. This creates common ground between people, but also gives rise to differences in ways of living, seeing, talking and thinking. This is what is meant by cultural diversity.

* Carers must be able to recognise difference and to acknowledge it in their practice; they must value diversity.

* The language used to talk about diversity is contentious and always evolving.

Study skills: Voices as 'source material'

On Audio Cassette 3 you hear people from a variety of Minority Ethnic groups speaking at length. This presents quite a rare opportunity. How often have you listened to the views of Gypsy Travellers? Every day, if you are a Gypsy Traveller yourself, but seldom, perhaps, if you are not. Although we live in a very diverse society, our personal lives probably give us contact with only a few sections of it. (Even if you meet a broad cross-section of people through your work, you will tend to be quite restricted in what you can talk to them about.) Of course you see and hear people from a range of different social groups on TV and in radio broadcasts – yet that does not really put you in touch with the full breadth of society. Members of some groups appear frequently through the mass media, but other groups are rarely represented – and when they do appear briefly, they are framed within programmes which ask particular questions and present particular 'angles', so you see and hear them in a very restricted way.

In other words, an audio cassette like this is a valuable resource. It enables you to hear voices directly – not interpreted by someone else with a point to make. You hear how other people view their circumstances and their lives – how they make sense of the world. It is very hard to acquire this depth of insight through print (except perhaps through novels), yet you pick it up very quickly as you listen. Of course, the speakers you hear are talking into a microphone, to an interviewer, with a sound recordist nearby – and they are answering questions – so it isn't 'normal conversation'. But they have enough time and scope to give a flavour of their particular way of looking at the world.

So the audio cassette is not simply 'more words to absorb'. It is *source material* for you to examine closely and think about. That is why we ask you to listen to it several times. You are listening not just to *what* is said, but also to what is *behind* the words – people's assumptions, attitudes, beliefs, ways of relating to society. You listen, not as a participant caught up in the emotions of a conversation, but as a detached 'observer' making a detailed analysis. (You could equally well analyse a recording of your own conversation with friends – there would be as much fascinating detail to uncover.) Social science enquiry often involves looking at very ordinary things in a lot of detail. It's what you look for and how you look that counts. Activity 2 is an introduction to that kind of analytical approach.

This section has taken you beyond some of the simplifications and introduced a small fragment of the rich diversity and complexity that make up 'culture' and 'ethnicity'. Culture may be associated with religion, nationality or social customs, as with Gypsy Travellers. In the complex tapestry of individual lives, people may find they have beliefs and ways of living in common with people who they think of as very different from themselves. For example, some Muslims who belong to different cultures and live in countries as diverse as Gambia and Iran are united by their faith. Other communities share a language and nationality but are divided by religious or sectarian divides such as in Northern Ireland.

Section 2
Stereotypes and prejudice

You looked for evidence of cultural 'difference' in Rita and Kathleen's lives, but you will also have heard something else. You heard them talking about other people's misunderstanding of their way of life. This is something that affects, for instance, the services they receive.

Activity 3 | Finding evidence of misunderstanding of needs

Allow about 10 minutes

Listen to Audio Cassette 3, side 1 again, and this time note down any examples you hear of the provision of services being affected by misunderstandings of Traveller culture.

Comments | Did you identify any examples of service providers misunderstanding the Traveller culture? The teacher from the education board seemed surprised that the caravan was not 'rotten' and 'filthy dirty', while the health visitor seemed to expect that gypsies would not understand basic baby care or have the resources to care adequately for a baby. Rita and Kathleen were also aware of prejudice against the practice of 'churching', which tended to be perceived as restrictive and oppressive to women.

Responding in a balanced and thoughtful way to apparently unjust treatment of a particular group is not easy. Some groups, such as women and disabled people, are disadvantaged in many cultures and societies and 'valuing diversity' does not mean that such injustices should be ignored. It is possible, however, to misinterpret injustice in other cultures. For example, the wearing of headscarves or 'hijab' has been disapproved of in French schools, but many Muslim girls and young women felt very positive about wearing their hijab and felt they were experiencing injustice from the schools, rather than from their religion. In the end injustice should be judged by those experiencing it *within* a culture, rather than from outside. In the case of Rita and Kathleen, they did not want to be 'rescued' from churching. They wanted services.

It is easy for care providers who are unfamiliar with a particular culture to misunderstand and make false assumptions about the needs of those seeking services. But often there is more to it than simple misunderstanding; the false assumptions follow a regular pattern because they are based on *stereotypes* and reflect *prejudices*.

Terminology Box 2: Stereotypes

Stereotyping is a process through which we ascribe a set of attributes to a person based on their presumed membership of a particular group. The significance of stereotyping is that the assumptions are not based on fact and do not stem from knowledge of the person in question, but are generalisations that may or may not be true but often have some grain of apparent truth. For example:

• Accountants are boring

• Welsh people are good singers

• *Guardian* readers are vegetarians.

Prejudice

Sometimes a stereotype is associated with a belief about whether the attributes linked to a particular group are generally positive or negative. This belief is called prejudice, and takes us beyond:

> *'Accountants are boring, but I don't mind boring'*

to:

> *'I hate accountants, they are all boring'.*

Everybody uses stereotypes; they are a way in which people 'make sense' of complex information. We also all have prejudices. Some people may arouse strong feelings in us according to the 'category' that we place them in. These feelings are based on the characteristics which we think everyone in that category has, rather than on the experience of knowing the individual.

Activity 4   What are your prejudices?

Allow about 10 minutes   Can you think of any prejudices that you hold? Try to make a list of them. Here are a few of mine!

- I think of smokers as weak-willed and pathetic for not giving up.
- I think of people who read certain newspapers as uncaring and complacent.
- I think of people who use mobile phones on the train as just showing off.

Comment   These may seem like minor irritations, but they are nevertheless prejudices – do you find that you attribute characteristics to people in these groups although the behaviour you observe does not justify such assumptions? I always feel that mobile phone users want everyone to hear how busy they are and what a great time they are having – I see them as wanting to draw attention to themselves. It could be that they just have an urgent call to make.

Your everyday prejudices might seem fairly harmless, but you are not in a position to judge how they affect other people. As a woman, I might find myself stereotyped as caring and emotional. While I would be happy to accept these qualities at times, I would also want people to see that I can be assertive and ambitious. Another person's stereotyped view of me may limit my options – especially if that person is my employer or my doctor. In fact your stereotype of me as a mother with young children may impose on me an alien identity in which I may not recognise myself.

In a similar way, terms such as 'Asian', 'immigrant' or 'asylum seeker' tend to carry with them fairly fixed images, ideas and beliefs about the characteristics of people belonging to such groups. Again you can see that people's perceptions of members of these groups are stereotyped, and to the extent that beliefs about them are not based on knowledge of real individual people, they are prejudiced. But what makes stereotyping and prejudice particularly significant in relation to these terms is that they are often linked to ideas about race.

Terminology Box 3: Race and racism

In this unit I shall generally be avoiding the use of the word *race*. We can talk meaningfully about different 'cultures' and different 'ethnicities', but there are heated arguments between scientists about whether it is ever possible to identify particular races, or to draw meaningful boundaries between them. In other words, the concept of race is of extremely doubtful use in serious argument.

However, what is not in doubt is that many people have *believed* that there are races and have often used the concept of race in ways that advantage some people and disadvantage others. In other words, they have been *racist*. To be racist is to think and act towards people in ways which are damaging to them and their interests, on the basis of *assumed* racial differences.

So, while *race* is a very doubtful concept and will not be used in this unit, *racism* is an extremely important concept and will be a central concern.

Differences and commonalities

We now move on to explore how stereotyping and prejudice can affect members of different Minority Ethnic groups, particularly in the context of their encounters with providers of care services.

Activity 5   Stereotypes of Asian families

Allow about 30 minutes

Now turn to Chapter 21 in the Reader by Robina Shah, '"He's our child and we shall always love him" – mental handicap: the parents' response', which is based on Shah's research into the needs of disabled children in Asian families. In this chapter Shah provides some examples of the kinds of assumption or stereotype about Asian women and Asian families that she has come across in her research work. She suggests that social workers' assessments may be based on ill-informed assumptions that misrepresent the realities of life for Asian families in Britain. Later, in the section headed 'Look behind the word Asian and see me', she lists further instances of stereotypical ideas of Asian parents' attitudes to disability.

Read Chapter 21 now. As you do so, note down your responses to the following:

(a)   In Shah's view, what damage does stereotyping do to Asian parents?

(b)   In what way does Shah see a connection between ethnic stereotyping and racism?

Comment   (a)   Shah suggests that stereotyping can be very damaging. She points to some of the problems, for both users and providers of services, of relying on stereotypes as a guide to action.

- First, stereotypes are broad generalisations which overlook individual differences within communities, depriving people, as Shah puts it, of their 'uniqueness'. As she says, Asian parents 'don't wish to be placed in the "pool of generalisations"' or have one person's experience 'speak for the whole Asian community'.

- Second, stereotypes tend to overlook similarities between ethnic groups and can lead to 'looking for differences where none exist'. These similarities might be between people who are 'white' and 'Black and Ethnic Minorities' as well as within these groups.

- Third, the process of stereotyping can lead to misinterpreting people's needs. An example Shah gives is the assumption that the absence of toys in the living room means that toys are not seen as important.

(b)   Shah places the process of stereotyping in the wider context of prejudice, discrimination and racism towards Minority Ethnic communities. She suggests that racism may be personal (the attitudes or actions of individuals) or institutional (resulting from a common set of beliefs within an institution or service provider). I will return to these concepts later in the unit.

Both illustrations demonstrate that holding stereotypical beliefs about the needs of a group of people based on race or ethnicity can lead to the provision of services which at best overlook or misunderstand the needs of individual members of these groups. At worst stereotyping and prejudice can lead to services which restrict people's rights and civil liberties.

Key points

- We are all prone to interpret the world in terms of stereotypes and to hold prejudices. However, unfamiliarity with a particular culture can lead to misunderstandings and false assumptions by care providers.

- Care workers' stereotyped views of people who belong to Black or Minority Ethnic groups can lead to inappropriate and inadequate service provision.

Section 3
Racial discrimination within care

3.1 Experiencing discrimination in a care environment

In Sections 1 and 2 you looked at the concepts of stereotyping, prejudice and diversity of cultures. Anyone can be the subject of prejudice, but this alone does not necessarily have a great impact on that person's life. The belief by some that accountants are boring will not in itself prevent accountants from fulfilling their aspirations, from making the most of their 'life chances'. Part of the reason for this is that the people who believe that 'accountants are boring' are not necessarily in a position to influence the life chances or opportunities of accountants. One way of assessing this is to measure opportunities against specific categories. Such categories might include being healthy and well nourished, living in secure and comfortable accommodation, receiving a successful education, being financially secure and being socially and intellectually stimulated (these categories broadly match Maslow's hierarchy of need which you encountered in Unit 3).

This section will begin by looking at the impact of discrimination on one particular little girl called Lorna. (You will meet Lorna again as a young woman in Section 4.)

Lorna Campbell: Part 1

Lorna and her brother Jason were the children of Deirdre and Benjamin Campbell. The Campbells moved to the UK from St Lucia in 1957 after Benjamin was offered work in the NHS as part of a government recruitment scheme under the British Nationality Act of 1948. This act encouraged economic migrants from Commonwealth territories to settle and work in the UK with their families to help combat post-war employment shortages. Both children were removed to local authority care (today this is called the 'Looked After System') when their mother died and Benjamin eventually felt unable to cope alone. Lorna was too young to be placed in the children's home with her brother, and spent the next 18 months of her life in a residential nursery. The nursery provided a short-term home for six babies who were cared for by 12 members of staff working seven hour shifts. Lorna and Jason had no contact with each other or with their father and Lorna did not find out where Jason spent his childhood.

When she was four Lorna was moved to The Lawns children's home with the intention that she be adopted. The Lawns was situated in a working class area of the city, where at the time there were few Black people. All the staff and other children at The Lawns were white. The 'problem' of Black and Minority Ethnic children was high on the agenda of the local social services department. It was felt that children such as Lorna would be best served by enabling them to be assimilated into what they saw as a common 'white' culture, as represented in the local community, and given the same opportunities as white children. Staff and children were discouraged from talking about Lorna's skin colour but Lorna often felt different from the other children and found it difficult to make friends.

When she was six Lorna did have a close friend, Rebecca, who lived at The Lawns for a short time before returning to her family. Rebecca and Lorna enjoyed making a secret 'camp' in the garden and collecting flowers and sticks to make pretend feasts for the birds and squirrels. At school Lorna was encouraged to join the athletics team; she resisted this as it clashed with biology classes which she enjoyed. Lorna's care workers and teachers repeatedly put pressure on her, reminding her that she would not be entered for the Biology GCSE and that she was both letting the school down and, as usual, being disruptive. On one occasion Lorna asked to have her hair braided, but this was refused on the grounds that other children had been refused perms due to cost. Lorna had no contact with Black culture or other Black children until she was in secondary school, where there were some children of Asian heritage. Lorna was shocked to be referred to by her white peers as a 'Pakki' and ignored by the Asian children. Lorna did not have anyone to talk to about her experience of racism. She did not know what racism was and was confused about the hostility she met at school.

Throughout her childhood Lorna's behaviour became of increasing concern to social workers. She was described as being 'aggressive and unco-operative'. Two placements with white foster carers were attempted, but both broke down with the foster carer complaining that Lorna's behaviour was unacceptable. As Lorna became increasingly 'difficult', her childhood was punctuated with emergency meetings to discuss her behaviour and where she should live. When she was 15 the local authority placed her with African Caribbean foster carers, who specialised in providing preparation for independent living for teenagers. This placement was a disaster; Lorna was verbally abusive to the carers, calling them 'niggers' and her foster mother a 'black bitch'. She rejected the carers' attempts to promote positive aspects of Black culture such as providing hair and skin products and refused to attend their Black church. Lorna told her social worker that she felt uncomfortable and out of place in an African Caribbean home. She said that she felt as if she was pretending to be someone she wasn't and was always being watched. Lorna continually ran away until she was two weeks from her 16th birthday, when she moved to live in bed and breakfast accommodation on her own.

Lorna playing with Rebecca

It is always very difficult separating emotional damage experienced as a result of discrimination from emotional damage to a child resulting from broken attachments. In Block 1 you read about the work of Bowlby (1953) and Rutter (1986) who suggested that in order for children to be able to learn to make trusting and rewarding relationships as they grow up, they need to have had a secure carer or a limited number of consistent carers. More recent research (Grotberg, 1995; Rutter, 1990) into the resilience of children has shown that some children can cope with significant trauma in their lives, yet these first, or *primary*, relationships remain very important. According to Grotberg (1995), the children who are likely to be more resilient are:

1   Children who have people around them whom they trust and who help them learn how to participate in society.

2   Children who feel loved, valued and respected as a person.

3   Children who are able to talk to someone and find help if they feel afraid.

Activity 6　Growing up with discrimination

Allow about 15 minutes　The table below has three columns. Each one represents one of Grotberg's three points, but I have slightly simplified them and made them specific to Lorna. Re-read the case study and as you read it note down any examples of these conditions *not* being met for Lorna.

Did Lorna have people around whom she trusted and who could be role models for her?	Did Lorna feel loved, valued and respected?	Did Lorna have someone she felt able to talk to and who would help her when she was afraid?

Comment　How did you get on? Did you feel that any of the examples you found related to Lorna being discriminated against on the basis of her culture and 'race'? I will give you some of my observations and we will then move on to explore the effect of racism on children in care in more depth.

Did Lorna have people around whom she trusted and who could be role models for her?	Did Lorna feel loved, valued and respected?	Did Lorna have someone she felt able to talk to and who would help her when she was afraid?
As a toddler Lorna had many carers, which would have made it difficult for her to build trusting relationships as she grew up. As a result Lorna did not have a single adult with whom she had consistent contact throughout her childhood.	The experience of rejection as Lorna moved between placements was likely to reinforce her feelings of not being valued. Why was she always moved on when other children were placed in permanent homes?	Lorna did not have people in her life whom she trusted and felt loved by — so who could she turn to when she felt afraid or needed help? Most children find themselves in 'trouble' at some time in their lives, and need a trusted person to help them find a solution to their problems.

Lorna had no role models in her life who shared her culture or heritage. Such role models might have helped her to learn to behave in a socially acceptable way. Instead she expressed her hurt and anger in a way which soon gained her the label of 'difficult and aggressive'.	The direct racism (such as name-calling) and indirect racism (such as ignoring her cultural needs) were likely to have had a negative effect on her self-respect and made her feel unvalued. When Lorna was eventually placed with carers who recognised her cultural needs she felt uncomfortable — as if she did not belong — and this made it difficult for her to feel loved and valued.	Lorna was perceived as 'different' by her carers. This is likely to have made it difficult for Lorna to seek help from adults around her as she may have felt that they would not understand her.
With nobody who could share her experience of being Black Lorna had no one to help her learn how to deal with racist attitudes or behaviour, or to reinforce a positive image of being Black. Lorna only had access to the media representation of Black people and the prejudices of white people she encountered. Unfortunately she was offered the opportunity of African Caribbean carers too late.	Lorna had no consistent loving relationships to enable her carers to really know and love her as an individual child. Instead she was seen as naughty and a troublemaker. Her closest relationship, with Rebecca, was sadly cut short due to Rebecca's change of placement.	Lorna did not find it easy to seek support from her peers; she was seen as different and the adults in her peers' lives did not help the children talk about cultural differences and racism.

You can see that Lorna was vulnerable in various ways, simply through being a young child in care. But she was made much more vulnerable because she was Black and this was not adequately taken into account by her carers. They tended to see her as a 'black child' and as a 'problem' rather than as Lorna, making her more isolated and unsupported at a time when children need lots of support. The emotional vulnerability which, according to theorists such as Bowlby (1953) and Rutter (1986), always accompanies disrupted infant 'attachments', was compounded by the additional isolation of:

- being seen in stereotyped ways as a black girl by those in charge of her, and

- prejudice from the other children, and also from her carers.

Whether it was intentional or not, she clearly experienced discrimination.

3.2 Discrimination and power

As a child, Lorna was all the more vulnerable to prejudice because of the enormous imbalance of power between her and her carers. The carers were in a position to determine everything about her immediate and future life chances through their policies and the decisions they made. Lorna also experienced prejudice – she was 'pre-judged' by her carers and peers. Lorna appeared to these people as a 'black child' rather than as 'Lorna' and from this view assumptions were made about who she was and what her needs were. While this might have been unpleasant and frustrating for Lorna, the impact of this prejudice would not have been so pervasive if there had not been an imbalance of 'power' between Lorna and those around her. By this I mean that other people, for different reasons, were in a position to be able to influence Lorna's life chances.

I would like you first to think about why Lorna was less 'powerful' than her carers, teachers and fellow school and house mates. She clearly had less power than the adults in her life as a result of being a child. Beyond this, however, she was in a 'minority' – her peers and carers shared stereotypical views about people from the Caribbean and may have had little contact with 'real' African Caribbean people, as opposed to media images to challenge their views. Alternatively, their stereotypical beliefs may have been reinforced by being shared with white members of the community, despite contact with Black and Minority Ethnic people. The reflection of stereotypical images in the media, as well as among people we talk to, strengthens our confidence that the stereotypes are, in fact, reality. Lorna's experience of being 'pushed' into athletics is an illustration of stereotypes being shared about African Caribbean people excelling in sports. While the actions of her teachers and carers might not have been intentionally harmful, they disregarded Lorna as an individual.

Stereotypes about Black and Minority Ethnic people are deeply embedded in many societies, stemming from beliefs that they are inherently inferior and 'different' from 'white' people. This can be seen in press reports on people who are seeking asylum in the UK, with the commonly held view that all such people are 'economic migrants' and therefore undesirable.

I would now like to turn to the professionals who had contact with Lorna – the social workers, residential workers and teachers – and look at the 'power' that they may have. Power was discussed briefly in Unit 4. One of the common ways in which providers of care services are able to be in a powerful position over service users is that they have access to specialist knowledge. Some providers, such as GPs and social workers, act as 'gatekeepers' to resources (as discussed in Unit 10). Other service providers do not have direct control over the accessing of services in this way, but they are in a position to influence the experience of receiving care, an area discussed in some depth in Block 1 in relation to intimate care and privacy. Frank Keating (cited in ILPS, 1993) suggests they exert three types of power:

Professional power: the status bestowed by society on people deemed to be professional such as doctors, nurses, social workers, teachers and solicitors. If you have recently applied for a passport you will have needed a 'professional' to sign your application; did you stop to wonder why someone belonging to one of these professions is deemed more trustworthy? Lorna's care was influenced by social workers and teachers who had the power to make important decisions about her life, such as where she lived and what subjects she took at school. Their 'professional' role gave them an authority to make decisions and influence the actions of others, regardless of Lorna's views.

Expert power: this relates to the power derived from access to knowledge; professionals have expert power but others may also become experts if they are able to access specialist knowledge. The Parkinson's patients described by Pinder in Unit 2 are good examples. Expert opinion while Lorna was growing up dictated that it was in the best interests of Black and Minority Ethnic children to be treated in the same way as white children. This 'colour-blind' approach resulted in carers ignoring Lorna's need for different care provision from her white peers. It validated her placement with white carers and the denial of provision that white children would not receive, such as having her hair braided.

Resource/coercive power: again many professionals also have this form of power which relates to the ability to 'gatekeep' resources or to compel people to behave in a particular way. While social workers and health professionals provide supportive services, they are also able to use legislation to control where children or mentally ill people live. Lorna experienced this form of power along with many other African Caribbean children in their overrepresentation in the Looked After System and the fact that they are less likely to be placed with foster carers or adopters who reflect their ethnicity. This is due both to resources, or rather the lack of resources to recruit and support such carers, and coercion, as Black and Minority Ethnic people are more likely to be on the receiving end of coercive, rather than supportive, services. If Lorna's father had been white he might, for example, have received more support as an alternative to Lorna being Looked After.

Activity 7   Power in care work

Allow about 10 minutes   Look at the following list of workers in health and social care, and try to note down three examples of how they might have 'power' over their service users or patients. One example for the GP might be that she can make the decision to refer a patient to a hospital or consultant.

- GP
- home care worker
- auxiliary nurse on a surgical ward.

Comment   The GP may initially seem to be the person with the clearest power – a professional with the specialist knowledge and authority to provide or withhold valuable and sometimes scarce resources. Did you think of ways in which the home care worker and auxiliary nurse have power? Although home care workers may not categorise themselves as 'professionals', they may still have access to specialist knowledge such as the availability of, and referral procedures for, alternative services. Both the nurse and the home care worker might find themselves in positions where they are caring for vulnerable people who depend on their integrity and respect and would not easily be able to complain or seek alternative service providers.

Lorna's life, therefore, unlike that of our imaginary accountant, was greatly affected by the way in which members of her community – people she lived with and went to school with – were in a position to influence her life. There is evidence to suggest that being Black or a member of a Minority Ethnic group clearly limits an individual's life chances.

Thompson (2000) suggests that this is also true of membership of other groups, such as being a woman, over 65 and/or disabled. Disadvantage for these groups is represented by factors such as lower incomes, poorer housing, poorer health and lower educational achievement. For other groups the evidence is less clear, but there are examples of specific situations in which prejudicial attitudes disadvantage members of certain groups. For example, there is no legislation outlawing prejudicial treatment against gay individuals in the employment situation; and non British Citizens resident in the UK do not have an automatic right to work, draw benefits or vote in elections. These factors also have an impact on people's life chances, or 'power'.

We have seen in Lorna's case, that where stereotypical assumptions and the negative beliefs that lead to prejudice are combined with the power to act, *discrimination* can occur. Look carefully at the following diagram developed by OSDC, which attempts to explain the process of discrimination.

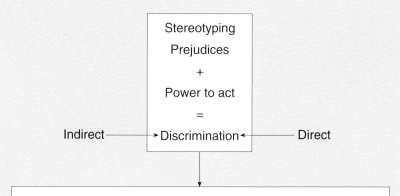

Figure 1 Adapted from Barn, Sinclair, Ferdinand (1997b) Understanding Racism and Developing Good Practice, *OSDC*

This diagram suggests how discrimination arises out of a combination of factors. The beginning of the process is the existence of stereotyping and prejudice in both individuals and more widely within organisations, such as hospitals or care agencies and society generally. When these attitudes and beliefs coincide with individuals and organisations having power to take action (such as making assessments, referrals to other resources or providing direct care) discrimination occurs, of either a direct or an indirect kind.

> **Terminology Box 4: Discrimination**
>
> Discrimination is the process of treating individuals differently, often unfavourably, based on prejudice. Discrimination can operate at a number of levels. It can be:
>
> *   **direct,** when it is an open action clearly intended to have an impact on the person to whom it is directed, or
>
> *   **indirect**, where it still has an impact but the action is less overt, perhaps unintentional.
>
> An illustration of direct racism would be refusing to provide a service for somebody on the basis of their 'race' or colour, or deliberately providing an inferior service.
>
> More commonly racism is indirect, for example, services are open to everyone, but the service is provided in such a way as to overlook the needs of some people, the majority of whom are Black. An example would be failing to provide halal meat for Muslim service users in a day centre – or failing to inform them that they have the right to request it. Discrimination can stem from inaction, failing to do something, as well as action, as described above.

While we have talked about discrimination experienced by people like Lorna who are on the receiving end of care services, at the same time we must recognise that discrimination is experienced by many care workers.

3.3 Black and Minority Ethnic care workers

Although care workers have access to power through their professional role, they may themselves experience the impact of discrimination within the care services. A study carried out by the Policy Studies Institute (Beishon, 1995) revealed the extent of discrimination experienced by nurses in the NHS. While there are large numbers of Black and Minority Ethnic nurses in the lower grades, they were underrepresented above grade E. A quarter of respondents believed that they had missed opportunities for being put forward for training or for recruitment and promotion, due to racism. A third of the sample reported experiencing racism from colleagues, while two-thirds had experienced racism from patients or families. This was of particular concern, as respondents also felt unsupported by employers when reporting harassment. Some even reported being 'replaced' by a white worker as a strategy to deal with a racist patient. For workers who may be in a minority, or in jobs lower down the hierarchy, taking action to combat racism may be difficult. Ironically, though, Gerrish *et al.* (1996) suggest that many Black and Minority Ethnic nurses and student nurses *only* experience being placed in the position of being an 'expert' on issues of ethnicity.

> *This places a considerable unreasonable burden on minority ethnic students and detracts from the need for such students to themselves develop the skills to work in a multi-ethnic population.*

> (Gerrish et al., 1996, p. 141)

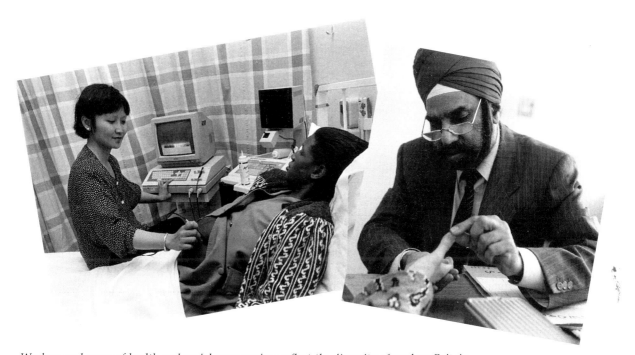

Workers and users of health and social care services reflect the diversity of modern Britain

The government has recognised that there is a problem and responded with the publication of *The Vital Connection* by the Department of Health (2000a). This document lays out a framework intended to enhance the recruitment, retention and development of underrepresented groups and to ensure that the NHS is a 'fair employer' (Culley and Dyson, 2001).

Key points

- Where stereotypes and prejudiced assumptions are held by people who have the power to influence lives (such as doctors or social workers) discrimination is very likely to occur.

- Members of Black and Minority Ethnic groups have experienced discrimination when employed as care workers as well as when they receive care.

- Membership of some social categories tends to result in having less power and poorer life chances.

Section 4

Care provision for Black and Minority Ethnic children and young people

4.1 Culture and identity

In Activity 6 we discussed the difficulties Lorna experienced in establishing a 'sense of herself' or what we can call her 'identity'. (Identity is an elusive concept which you will look at again in Block 4.) Various researchers have reported that Black children grow up with poor self-esteem. For example, in experiments where Black children were asked to choose between white and black dolls, more chose white, which was taken as an indication that they themselves would prefer to be white (Clark and Clark, 1939, 1947; Pushkin, 1973; Davey, 1983 – all cited in Owusu-Bempah). However, this research has been put in doubt by more recent studies. Concern has been raised that as a result of the earlier research social workers are more likely to explain the Black child's difficulties as being related to racial and cultural identity needs, while for the white child other explanations were offered (Owusu-Bempah, 1994).

There has been considerable research into the experiences of Black and Minority Ethnic children in care which suggests that Lorna's experiences are not unusual (Dwivedi and Varma, 1996; Ahmad, 1996; Dominelli, 1988). Black and Minority Ethnic children are twice as likely to be looked after by the local authority (Department of Health, 1999). Research in one London borough in the mid-1980s found that Black children constituted 52 per cent of the borough's children in care although they formed 40 per cent of the child population (Barn, cited in Skellington, 1996). Over half of these children were of African-Caribbean origin. Barn claimed that Black children were admitted into care 'from situations where preventive strategies could have been attempted' and found that Black children entered care more quickly than white children:

> Barn's study ... demonstrated the important role racial stereotypes play in pathologising black families ... Barn explained differences in the referral and admission patterns of black and white children in terms of social workers' perceptions of individual cases set against the context of the disadvantaged position of black families in the areas of housing and employment and the greater likelihood of such families needing social services help.
>
> (Skellington, 1996, p. 128)

Here Barn is reminding us that due to discrimination, Black and Minority Ethnic families may be more likely to be coping with the stress of poor housing, unemployment and low wages. However, the apparently high numbers of Black and Minority Ethnic families coming to the attention of social workers may feed into negative 'racial stereotypes', suggesting, for example, that the parents are inadequate or even abusive. It is, however, the economic and environmental factors which create difficulties for parents and their children rather than the quality of the adults' 'natural' parenting abilities. Barn argues that if social workers focused more on support aimed at alleviating the practical problems, they could eliminate the need for some children to be separated from their parents.

While research has indicated that African Caribbean families have been over represented in the Looked After System, this is not a universal picture. Patel and Singh (1998) noted that in Scotland children from Black and Minority Ethnic communities were not visible in social work services, but they were unable to confirm whether this was due to negative stereotypes such as 'they look after their own' or because they were unaware of support.

The opportunity of being offered a secure permanent placement is often (although not always) the best outcome for children who are unable to live with their birth family. In addition to not being offered a placement which reflected her ethnic or cultural needs, Lorna also experienced the trauma of multiple unstable placements. Research by the British Association of Adoption and Fostering (BAAF) suggests that Black and Minority Ethnic children are less likely to be adopted than white children and where they are adopted they will wait significantly longer for a placement.

In their sample of children awaiting adoption, researchers identified that 90 per cent of adopted children were white, while of the Minority Ethnic children who were placed for adoption 75 per cent were of mixed parentage (in other words, one of their natural parents was 'white') (Jackson, 2001). Of children over 30 months, white girls were placed with adopters in a significantly shorter time than other children. Black and mixed parentage children, older boys and children with developmental delay and medical problems waited longer at each stage of the adoption process.

The overrepresentation of Black children in the care system is obviously a matter of great concern. However, it is even more worrying when we consider the research on the prospects for young people leaving care, who are disadvantaged in terms of health, housing, employment and poverty. We will return to this issue in Section 4.

Black and Minority Ethnic children cared for away from birth parents and placed with carers who do not match their ethnicity do not necessarily fail to have their needs met. A summary of research by Harry Zeitlin (1996) suggested that children who were transracially adopted (adopted by parents of a different 'race' from themselves) did not necessarily have a worse outcome than racially-matched placements. In part this was due to the rather crude reliance on 'race' as a factor, which does not take account of other important criteria such as culture and socio-economic group. More importantly for social workers planning placements, the research highlighted some key issues which influenced the outcome for children. These included:

• a strong relationship with the adoptive parent

• positive reinforcement of the child's abilities

• assistance in talking about race

• expressing racial ambivalence (Zeitlin, 1996, p. 73).

This research is contentious as government policy and legislation encourages matching race and culture, but it does highlight some positive practices where transracial placements are made.

Mehra (1996), writing about Minority Ethnic children in residential care, reinforces this by suggesting that placements should enable children:

1   To develop a positive identity for him/herself as an ethnic minority child.

2   To develop the necessary linguistic, cultural, religious and social skills to function effectively as an adult in a multiracial multicultural society.

3   To acquire skills to cope as both child and adult in a society in which the child is likely to encounter racism, prejudice and disadvantage.

4   To enable the child to come to terms with living apart from its birth family.

(Mehra, 1996, p. 79)

Activity 8

Allow about 10 minutes

Building a positive sense of self

Spend 10 minutes reviewing the Lorna case study. Using the four points identified by Mehra, note down some suggestions of how Lorna's carers could have supported the development of a positive sense of herself as a young Black woman, ready for when she leaves public care.

Comment

Some of the points that you might have identified are:

• Lorna could have had contact with more staff and young people who reflected her 'race' or her culture, particularly earlier in her childhood.

• Her carers could have acknowledged Lorna's race and culture and discussed it with her.

• Lorna could have been provided with access to information about her culture, language or religious practices and given the opportunities to draw on these in the development of her own sense of who she is as an individual.

• Lorna could have been provided with the opportunity to talk about and develop skills to assist her in managing racism, prejudice or discrimination when she encountered it.

You may have thought of several more ideas.

4.2 Dual heritage children

The term 'dual heritage' refers to children who have parents of different 'heritage' – or 'race'/culture; you may be more familiar with the term 'mixed parentage' or 'mixed race'. 'Half caste' is also still in common use, although offensive to many people. These terms are generally used to refer to children who have one 'black' and one 'white' parent. Dual 'heritage', as opposed to 'parentage' or 'race', has come into more recent use to encompass children who may have parents who are both 'white' (or both 'black'), but nevertheless have a different heritage and culture. This move recognises that it is not only Black and Minority Ethnic children who have cultural needs, and that there can be cultural differences or conflicts between Black and Minority Ethnic parents who have different heritages. Research has increasingly raised concerns that this group of children is particularly vulnerable in the Looked After System.

Study skills: Honing your reading technique

How is your reading technique developing? Do you feel you are understanding enough, remembering enough, getting it done quickly enough? In the next two activities you will read articles from the Offprints book. How will you set about the task?

• Will you take a quick look through first to see what it seems to be about? Will you read just once, underlining key words as you go?

• How will you use the questions posed in the activities? Will you have them on a piece of paper and write down answers as you come to them? Will you wait until the end to try to answer them? Will you ignore them?

• What notice will you take of the 15 minute target time? What if the article takes you longer – will you stop at half an hour and just glance quickly ahead to check what the rest is about and then return to the unit? Will you see how interesting the reading is before deciding?

There are no 'correct' answers to these questions. You have to keep asking yourself what works for you in the light of what you want out of the course and what time you have available for studying.

When you have finished the reading, come back to this box and check off what the answer turned out to be. Then think what you have learnt about your current reading technique.

Activity 9   **Children of mixed parentage**

Allow about 15 minutes

Read the article in the Offprints entitled 'Children of mixed parentage'. What do Bola and Charmaine's stories tell us about the complexity of dual heritage children's placement needs?

Comment   This article highlights the fact that not only are all children individuals, rather than members of 'a Minority Ethnic community', but that their identity needs are not just about 'race'. Our identities are complex and change as a result of experiences and relationships in our lives. Identity includes our gender, culture and many other social 'ways of being' with which we associate ourselves.

Activity 10   **Am I a 'banana'?**

Allow about 30 minutes

You should now read the short article by Janis Fook in the Offprints. It should take about 15 minutes to read. What do you think Janis Fook's ideas add to our understanding of cultural and racial identity?

Comment   Janis Fook is talking about another dimension of cultural and racial difference; she lives with her birth family and is an Australian citizen who has no other language and no experience of living in a different culture. She feels Australian, but is treated as a racial minority. Being called a 'banana' implies that if you peel back her surface identity you would reveal her true identity. On reflection this makes Janis feel as if she is being treated as a fraud – not really Australian, not really Chinese. But Janis is really Janis. Her family culture reflects their own life experiences, influenced by a Chinese heritage, and by living in Australia for two generations. Her identity also encompasses everything else: her work, her gender, her social class, her beliefs and values.

4.3 Children leaving care

Let us return to Lorna as she leaves the Looked After System. How do you think her experiences of being an African Caribbean child in care might affect her life chances? As we have seen, research shows that Black and Minority Ethnic children fare worse than white children when cared for away from home. On top of that, all young people leaving care have significantly worse life chances than children who remain living at home. They leave 'home' at a younger age and have less support in their early adulthood than children outside the Looked After System. So we should think of Lorna simply as a care leaver first – before we consider the impact of her experiences as a Black or Minority Ethnic child.

The BAAF and the Department of Health have recently published research on the life chances of care leavers:

- *As many as 75 per cent of care leavers leave with no educational qualification, compared with 6 per cent for all school leavers (Department of Health, 2000, cited on http://www.baaf.org.uk [accessed 1.4.01]).*

- *12 per cent of children leaving care go on to further education compared to 68 per cent in the general population (BAAF, http://www.baaf.org.uk [accessed 1.4.01]).*

- *Up to 50 per cent of young people leaving care are unemployed (Department of Health, 2000, cited on http://www.baaf.org.uk [accessed 1.4.01]).*

- *Up to 20 per cent of young people experience homelessness within two years of leaving care (Department of Health, 2000, cited on http://www.baaf.org.uk [accessed 1.4.01]).*

Government concerns about the education of children in the care system led to the publication *Guidance on the Education of Children and Young People in Public Care* (Department of Health/Department for Education and Employment, 2000) which outlines action intended to address the problem of the poor educational experiences of children and young people in the Looked After System. This includes greater support for children within school and also improved communication between agencies such as schools, social services and foster carers.

The Children (Leaving Care) Act was launched in October 2001, placing additional responsibilities on local authorities to offer support to care leavers up until the age of 21. This legislation is supported by two policy initiatives in England and Wales respectively which give priority to care leavers. Quality Protect (England) and Children First (Wales) set objectives for local authorities to achieve in relation to specific areas of children's provision such as family support, looked after children and care leavers.

To summarise, research clearly demonstrates that all children leaving care are disadvantaged compared with those leaving 'home' and the government has made a commitment to tackle this inequality. The overrepresentation of African Caribbean children in the Looked After System means that these children are also likely to be overrepresented in terms of disadvantaged life chances when leaving care.

Key points

- All children need secure relationships to help them cope with crises or difficult experiences.

- Black and Minority Ethnic children receive a different response to their needs which can result in failure to meet these needs.

- Meeting the needs of children of dual heritage requires care workers to take account of the full complexity of identity development.

- All care leavers are at risk of serious disadvantage, and African Caribbean young people are overrepresented in this group.

Section 5
The impact of racism

5.1 Implications for practice

So far in this unit we have looked at what we mean by culture and at the diversity that exists within communities. We have also reflected on the way in which stereotypes and prejudice can have an impact on the services provided for Black and Minority Ethnic people and the consequent discrimination and disadvantage they experience. In this section we will consider a new term, 'institutional racism', and the way in which the delivery of care can be influenced by racism beyond the level of what individual people think, say or do.

We begin by returning to Lorna, now a young woman with children.

Lorna Campbell: Part 2

Lorna Campbell is now 27. She moved to the inner city in her late teens and made some contacts with the African Caribbean youth culture. Lorna has a sporadic relationship with a man who has fathered her four children: Mia is eight months, Emmanuel is two, Leah is five and Dean is seven years old. This man does not live with Lorna and she keeps him at a distance from herself and her children. They have a positive relationship but it suits both of them to live independently – Lorna finds the intimacy of living with a partner difficult. All four children were removed from their mother following an incident in which Lorna pushed Dean down the stairs of their maisonette. Dean suffered a dislocated and fractured arm and a minor head injury. The incident arose when Lorna was trying to get the children ready for bed and wanted Dean to help; he was running up and down the landing laughing and throwing toys. Lorna lost her temper and having grabbed Dean and pushed him, she then left the house for three hours. A neighbour found the children alone.

The situation was considered so serious that the local authority is considering whether or not the children should be returned to Lorna. All the children except Dean are living with a white foster carer. Dean is living with a white foster mother and an African Caribbean foster father. The younger children have some contact with Lorna, with a social worker supervising them, but Dean is refusing to see his mother. Concern about Lorna's parenting has been heightened by Lorna physically attacking social workers involved with her on three separate occasions. All of these attacks were sparked off by decisions being made about her children's care without her consent, such as attending school clubs or having school photos taken. Following the final assault on a social worker, which involved breaching bail conditions, all contact between Lorna and her children has been suspended pending a court hearing to decide whether the children should be placed permanently away from their mother.

Activity 11   Reflection on Lorna's experiences

Allow about 5 minutes   This is perhaps the most distressing and shocking part of Lorna's story. Before we look at this in more detail, spend 5 minutes jotting down your own initial response to this section of the case study. What factors do you think might have contributed to Lorna getting into this terrible situation with her children?

Comment   Your responses will depend on your individual perspective. From such a limited case study and without getting to know Lorna there is no way of *knowing* why she acted as she did. There are, however, some hypotheses (mini-theories) which could be considered. A recent document (*The Children Act Now: Messages for policy and practice,* 2001)) published by the Department of Health, summarises some of the ideas that have developed from research about why parents might be at risk of harming their children. This document suggests that parenting, social isolation and marginalisation are key factors.

Parenting

Lorna has had very little experience of positive models of parenting. She was with her mother for a very short period of time, during which her mother was unwell. Lorna subsequently moved between a number of carer situations, most of which were not in a 'family' context. Research suggests that the absence of positive parenting relationships as a child can lead to harmful or unresponsive parenting as an adult, though this is by no means always the case (Schaffer, 1992). Parents who did not have a positive parenting experience can overcome this 'risk factor'. Equally there are many other factors which can influence the quality of parent-child relationships. Research for the Department of Health report suggests that parents would both benefit from and welcome services aimed at supporting their development of parenting skills. Strategies aimed at early intervention with new parents, such as Sure Start, were noted to be of particular benefit. The report also noted that parents' own needs must be assessed and addressed to enable them to meet their children's needs.

Social isolation

This is one of the most frequently reported characteristics of families in which there is concern about parenting. Lorna's experiences may have made it difficult for her to develop supportive networks in her community. Like other care leavers, she will not have had 'parent figures' to return to after leaving home, who could support her in establishing a new life. She will also have had to make contacts in her new community without the benefit of contacts which other young people may have maintained, such as their parents and school friends. Lorna may also have experienced poverty, both through being a single parent and as a care leaver; 'living in enduring poverty remains a major problem for many of the families of children in need and places them at risk of being socially excluded' (Department of Health, 2001, p. 146).

Marginalisation

The Department of Health report suggested that there were many examples of 'parents who felt marginalised and degraded, especially those who were involved in care proceedings and whose children were looked after' (Department of Health, 2001, p. 142). This sense of degradation experienced when services become punitive and controlling is a strong feature of the experiences of Black and Minority Ethnic service users. Some researchers have reported that Black and Minority Ethnic families are assessed differently from white families in the investigation of parenting. They argue that stereotypical views of Black and Minority Ethnic families have been associated with the overrepresentation of these children in the Looked After System and also with excessively drastic interventions by health and social services.

In both parts of Lorna's story you have come across examples of intervention being 'controlling' rather than supportive:

- Lorna and Jason were removed from their father, rather than services being provided to enable them to remain at home while their father was supported in the community.

- Lorna was labelled as 'difficult and aggressive' and her behaviour was seen as a sign that she needed to be 'controlled', not as a cry for help from a child who felt that she was rejected and treated as different.

- As a young parent, Lorna's behaviour was 'pathologised'; she was treated as an intrinsically aggressive and dangerous person, unsafe to be allowed to care for her children. She was not provided with support to address her needs as a young woman who had experienced a difficult childhood, who was isolated in her community and marginalised by providers of services.

Lena Dominelli claims that racism 'operates through two channels which shape client–worker interactions: the exclusive channel and the inclusive one'. The exclusive channel results 'in black people having limited access to the "goodies" or caring services provided through social work intervention'; while the inclusive channel has produced a situation, Dominelli claims, in which Black people are overrepresented in services which 'are more directly engaged in controlling people's behaviour' (Dominelli, 1992, pp. 165–6).

Activity 12   Experiencing the 'two channels'

Allow about 10 minutes   (a)   Note down any examples you can recall from earlier in this unit of the exclusive channel in health and social care services – in other words, of members of Minority Ethnic groups being denied access to services they need – the exclusive channel.

(b)   Use any examples you have to suggest those areas of social work practice where Black people and other Minority Ethnic groups might be overrepresented – the inclusive channel.

Comment   (a)   In the exclusive channel you might have noted the absence of placements reflecting the needs of Black children, and poor assessments of the needs of Asian families based on a lack of cultural understanding. Dominelli also notes that Black elders are also underrepresented among people receiving home helps and sheltered accommodation.

(b)   On the inclusive side, you might have noted that Black children are more likely to enter the Looked After System and are more likely to do so under a court order. This might suggest to you that Minority Ethnic groups are more likely to be labelled and policed by professionals. Black people are overrepresented in areas where social workers have a 'policing' or 'controlling' role, such as putting children into care and assisting in admissions to psychiatric hospitals.

Throughout Lorna's life she has seen more of the punitive and controlling aspects of health and social care services than the supportive aspects. The next activity explores one of the reasons why this might have been the case.

Activity 13   Working with African Caribbean families

Allow about 15 minutes   Listen to Audio Cassette 3, Section 2, in which Lynthia Grant, a project worker for an organisation called Moyenda talks about the work of the project. Moyenda works to challenge racist attitudes towards Black families. As you listen, make a note of the stereotypes of Black families mentioned by Lynthia.

(NB: In this audio recording Lynthia uses the term 'Black' referring primarily to African Caribbean people; in my comment I will follow her convention.)

Comment   Lynthia says that the project sees its role as challenging the stereotyped negative images of Black families that exist, even among professionals. The common image is one of 'a very dysfunctional family', which includes the idea that Black families produce boys who end up as 'muggers' or in prison. She emphasises the need for service providers to focus on the strengths of Black families when carrying out assessments and also to recognise the need for Black parents to combat the assault on their children's self-esteem from racist images and beliefs. Lynthia also suggests that racism and the pressure to assimilate white cultural norms affects Black parents' confidence. In particular she suggests that Black parents may have different parenting priorities depending on their culture, such as emphasising responsibility, respect and discipline.

Family life

A survey carried out by Moyenda of 241 Black parents living mainly in Greater London and surrounding counties demonstrates that Lorna is not a typical example of a Black family:

- *The survey findings challenged the view that there are high rates of family breakdown and single parenting within the black communities. The researchers found well over half (60 per cent) of parents were married and 6 per cent were living with a partner. Only a third could be classified as 'lone parents', and these included 22 per cent who were single, 8 per cent who were separated, 2 per cent who were widowed and just 1 per cent who stated that they were divorced. The researchers concluded that the majority of black children in this sample were being brought up in a two-parent family home.*

* *The widely held view that large families are the norm among black people also did not hold true. Twenty per cent of parents were identified with four or more children. The majority (55 per cent) had no more than two children, of whom 22 per cent had just one child.*

(Moyenda, 1995, p. 39)

Moyenda's research also considered generational variations in parenting attitudes:

Work revealed variations in parenting attitudes and ideas amongst African-Caribbean parents and the concept of the African-Caribbean parent being 'strict and unbending' was challenged. Parents who were born here or came to the UK at an early age were very different in their thinking about parenting compared with parents who had spent a large part of their childhood in the Caribbean, where the concept of 'family' was perceived to be much broader than in Britain.

(Moyenda, 1995, p. 34)

These examples of changes across the generations are evidence of the complex differences between people which are overlooked in stereotypical generalisations about 'the Black family'. As with the Gypsy-Traveller and Asian cultures, beliefs and ways of life are not static or homogenous, and they are influenced by wider social change. We should never think of cultures either as fixed in time, or as having clear boundaries, whether or not they be Minority Ethnic cultures. As Black sociologist Paul Gilroy says:

'I think we need to be ... clear that no single culture is hermetically sealed off from others ... There can be no neat and tidy pluralistic separation of racial groups in this country ... Culture, even the culture which defines the groups we know as races, is never fixed, finished or final. It is fluid, it is actively and continually made and re-made.'

(Gilroy, 1992, p. 57)

Key points

* Some 'cultures' are given a privileged status in society; if you do not belong to these cultures you may experience a lack of understanding and even hostility.

* Prejudice has resulted in many Black and Minority Ethnic service users experiencing more controlling and less supportive provision from health and social care services.

5.2 Institutional racism

In this section of the unit we have spent time thinking about the way in which misrepresentations of Black and Minority Ethnic people and their cultures can have a serious impact on the services they receive. The power of these misrepresentations and beliefs stems partly from the authority of some of the professionals who share them, but more importantly from the way in which such beliefs are shared and perpetuated within organisations.

I would like you to think back to Lorna's experiences of living in a children's home. Many of the examples of discrimination which she encountered were not solely due to the attitudes of individual people involved in her care, but involved agency policies or 'institutional practices'. Here are some examples:

The 'policy' decision not to fund hair braiding. While this may seem comparable with a white child having a perm, the significance to Lorna as an African Caribbean was different. For Lorna, having her hair braided would have been an expression and affirmation of her heritage and culture, a culture which was not significantly represented in other ways in her home or community. This incident is an example of what Dominelli (1988) calls the 'colour blind' approach to meeting the needs of Black and Minority Ethnic people. By treating everyone 'equally', service providers are actually ignoring the very different and specific needs of Black and Minority Ethnic people. In order to avoid this, service providers must be aware of differences in need. They also need to take action to counter discrimination and inequality.

- This 'colour blind' attitude was something which Lorna encountered in all the people she met, including care staff and other children. This is important because it meant Lorna had no 'alternative view' to soften the impact, but also because such views are reinforced because they are commonly held.

- Lorna was not placed with carers who reflected her culture or heritage. This issue is not only about Black and Minority Ethnic children being placed only with Black and Minority Ethnic carers. Some writers have suggested that only Black and Minority Ethnic carers are in a position to prepare children for facing the racism they will encounter in their lives (Small, 1984; Thoburn, 1988). While Black and Minority Ethnic carers are certainly in a strong position to do this, it is also important to recognise that children's cultural needs are complex and do not just lie in their colour. You came across this complexity in Activity 6 in Section 3.

These examples illustrate the way in which discrimination is often more complicated and far-reaching than just prejudice on the part of individual people. Where discriminatory behaviour is built into the shared beliefs and practices of an organisation or institution, the effects can be drastic and all-encompassing, partly due to the power and reach of some organisations. You looked at the power of individuals in Section 3 and have also been introduced to some of the specific powers held by statutory health and care workers, such as involuntary admission to hospital and the removal of children from their parents. Where discrimination within institutions is based on racism, it is called 'institutional racism'.

> **Terminology Box 5: Institutional racism**
>
> You may have heard the term 'institutional racism', which came into the public consciousness with the publication of the Macpherson Report on the death of Stephen Lawrence. According to Macpherson:
>
> 'Institutional racism' consists of the collective failure of an organisation to provide an appropriate and professional service to people because of their colour, culture or ethnic origin. It can be seen or detected in processes, attitudes and behaviour which amount to discrimination through unwitting prejudice, ignorance, thoughtlessness, and racist stereotyping which disadvantage minority ethnic people (cited in Marlow and Loveday, 2000).
>
> Institutional racism is now a key concept for providers of health and social care. It has been highlighted in several recent reports, such as *Excellence not Excuses: Inspection of services for ethnic minority children and families* (Department of Health, 2000b). This report comments that:
>
> 'It would appear that society as reflected by public bodies, has not responded positively to the diverse groups of people of black origins who were born, or have made their homes, in this country. The challenge for individuals and institutions is to value the diversity of the population and work towards the elimination of racism' (Department of Health, 2000b, pp. 3–16)

The Macpherson Report led to the Racial Equality (Amendment) Act 2000 which extended the laws on racial discrimination to public authorities (such as the police, social services and health trusts). The Act also placed a duty on such bodies to eliminate racial discrimination and promote positive relations between racial groups. If the Act had been in force during Lorna's childhood care workers would have had the duty to challenge and counter the racist comments and behaviour of Lorna's peers as well as to re-examine their own practices.

Whether institutional racism is intentional or not, and whether it is conscious or not, it has a potentially devastating effect on individuals' lives – particularly where it is embedded within the 'culturally' accepted belief systems of organisations with responsibility not only for providing services but also for offering protection and implementing controls over the lives of people. The knowledge and beliefs on which action and practices are based ought to take account not only of cultural diversity, but also of the imbalance of power and advantage experienced by Black and Minority Ethnic people. We have seen in the experiences of Lorna and her children how the impact of discriminatory practices can continue from one generation to the next and how the effects of racism can be perpetuated within families.

> **Key points**
> - Racism goes beyond individual words and actions; it operates implicitly through the organisations and institutions of society.
> - Racism can be perpetuated by shared beliefs and prejudices held within organisations and institutions, including providers of health and social care.

Section 6
Responding to racism

6.1 Positive approaches to working with diverse communities

In this final section we look at some of the ways care providers can make their services more sensitive to diverse needs and we also look at techniques to help combat oppressive practices. You have already come across some positive interventions such as the work of Dostiyo in promoting positive images of African Caribbean families and also Mehra's ideas on promoting resilience in children. The Race Relations (Amendment) Act 2000 places a duty on public employees such as care workers and nurses to combat racism. Social workers in training have to demonstrate that they are able to 'identify, analyse and take action' to counter discrimination and racism (CCETSW, 1995). This means that they have a duty not only to recognise discriminatory 'processes, attitudes and behaviour' (Marlow and Loveday, 2000) but to understand why discrimination takes place and to take action to prevent it.

Terminology Box 6: Anti-discriminatory practice

This is a term used to describe a particular way of working, primarily within social work, whereby workers are expected to challenge and work towards eliminating discrimination, including racism. This responsibility does not stop with social workers' personal interaction with Black and Minority Ethnic people, but also includes the expectation that they take action to counter any discrimination or racism that they might encounter with white colleagues and service users.

Activity 14   **Am I black or am I white?**

Allow about 15 minutes   Read the poem below, which has strong resonances of Lorna's experiences as a child. As a residential social worker in Lorna's children's home, what do you think you could have done to try and 'take action' to counter the discrimination she experienced?

Am i black or am i white?

Am i black or am i white?
I used to ask that question
Every day and night
Why do you ask a question
As obvious as that?
It's plain to see that you are black.

But being in care
In a white community
It's hard to decide
with no black family.

For 15 years i never plaited or
combed my hair,
pulling out the tangles i
could just about bare.

Who are Rastafarians?
What is Reggae?
How can i understand
If no one will say?

The only black people i did see
Were tribes in Africa on TV
Or the big fat mamma striving
As a maid
For the white people only to degrade.

Leaving care i'm where i should be,
Living in the black community.

Margaret Parr

Comment   Did this poem give you ideas about what a care worker might have done to support Lorna? While it is a moving poem, it also refers to some very practical issues which could have been addressed:

- I have already challenged the failure of Lorna's carers to recognise the cultural importance of being allowed to have her hair braided. The poet reminds us that hair care is also a practical issue, and that children need carers who understand how to care for 'African Caribbean' hair. As a carer, if you did not have this knowledge you could take Lorna to a specialist hairdressers to ask for advice.

- Lorna needed the opportunity to live with carers who reflected her culture and also understood what it was like to live with racism. Again, as an individual care worker you may not be in a position to provide this placement or to meet these needs yourself. You could advocate for Lorna to have an independent visitor who did meet these needs; this is a provision for Looked After children in the Children Act 1989.

- Lorna needed the opportunity to learn about different cultures, particularly those that reflected her own heritage. As the poem suggests, it is not sufficient to see only common media images of Black and Minority Ethnic people, as they are either absent from view or stereotyped images such as the 'black fat mama' or 'tribes in Africa'. As a care worker you could have helped Lorna to have positive experiences of African Caribbean culture through books, music, festivals and making personal contacts in the community.

Activity 15   Working positively with cultural difference

Allow about 20 minutes   Listen to Audio Cassette 3. As you listen:

Try to identify examples of cultural differences *within* the Asian community. Also note down any examples of how Dostiyo is trying to *empower* Asian women (see Section 3 for an explanation of empowerment).

Comment   How did you get on?

(a) **Cultural differences**

There were a number of differences identified by Kalpana. Indeed, she stressed the need to be aware of the diversity of beliefs and practices within the so-called 'Asian community'. Individuals may be perceived from outside as belonging to a homogeneous community, even though they may have different religions, different nationalities, and belong to different socio-economic groups and different generations. From Dostiyo's work, for example, it was clear that services were provided primarily for men and therefore did not meet the needs of Asian women. In fact, the Young Asian Women in Crisis Project was set up to address the needs of younger generations of women whose culture had moved on from that of previous generations.

The message from Kalpana Desai is that providers of services need to be aware of cultural differences, but also to avoid making generalisations about the cultures of people who belong to a perceived 'ethnic group'. As you saw at the beginning of this unit 'culture' is complex and people's experience of it is very individual. It is important to remember that there are as many differences *within* any group as there are *between* groups. While it is useful to have some awareness of the possible areas in which care workers should be sensitive – such as diet, intimate care and arrangements for religious worship – it will always be necessary to find out from each *individual* person what is important for them. Care workers might try to teach themselves about a particular religion such as Islam, for example, but they will still need to check with each individual how their own practise of Islam might determine the way in which they need care to be provided.

Another area where assumptions cannot be made is in relation to language. It will be important to find out whether any service user (not only Black and Minority Ethnic people) speaks a common language with the care provider. Kalpana drew attention to the fact that recent arrivals to the UK, such as members of the Bangladeshi community, could be particularly isolated due to the fact that they may not yet be able to communicate in English in order to find out about services.

(b) **Empowerment**

Did you hear any examples of Dostiyo attempting to empower Asian women? Kalpana began by highlighting the importance of consulting the community about the services that they need rather than making assumptions. The Bangladeshi project was a good example of how the sharing of information can increase power; for them the need was for information and services to be provided in a language that they could understand. 'Provision of information' can take the form not only of making people aware of the availability of resources, but also of giving them access to 'specialist knowledge' which enables them to participate in planning and providing services. (Remember the experience of Pinder's patients with Parkinson's disease.)

6.2 Cultural competence

The focus within the nursing profession has been on a 'cultural competence' or 'cultural safety' model of practice. This model is based on an understanding that in order to provide safe and competent health services, practitioners need to have knowledge and understanding of people from diverse 'ethnic' or cultural backgrounds. The emphasis in this model is on developing knowledge which is cultural or 'ethnic' specific, particularly in terms of diseases or disease patterns but also in terms of lifestyle and beliefs. Papadopoulos *et al.* (1998) describe a four-staged model moving from cultural awareness to knowledge to sensitivity and finally arriving at cultural competence.

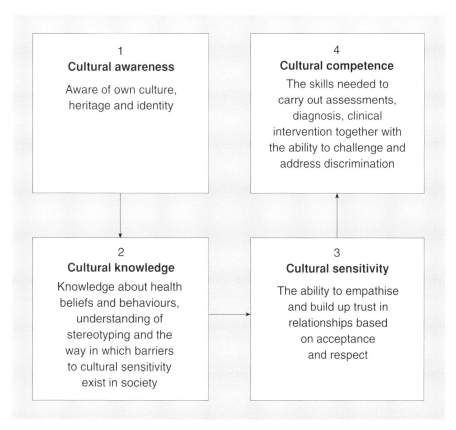

Figure 2 Cultural competence (adapted from Papadopoulos et al.*, 1998)*

The key features of cultural competence, therefore, are that it involves gaining knowledge about the way in which people of different ethnicities might have different needs and ensuring that responsibility for this goes beyond individual staff to the wider organisation.

6.3 Levels of influence

Challenging discrimination and racism is by no means an easy task, and Thompson (2000) suggests that our ability to influence the attitudes and behaviour of others diminishes as our contact with individuals becomes more remote. Thompson proposes a model referred to as P,C,S or Personal, Cultural, Structural.

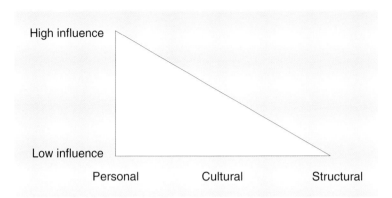

Figure 3 Analysis of anti-discriminatory practice (adapted from Thompson, 1998)

The **personal** level refers to the one-to-one encounters people have as individuals with family, friends, colleagues or service users. This is the level at which we are most influenced by the beliefs of other people, and are likely to be able to challenge their behaviour and beliefs. The **cultural** level represents the common beliefs and practices we encounter in cultures to which we belong or have contact with. These are still influential, although less so than individual encounters. At this level it starts to become more difficult to change beliefs and practices. Finally the **institutional** level; this refers to the 'structures' within society: the organisations, policies and legislation. Individuals are governed by these structures, but they have a more remote influence on our belief systems and as individuals we will struggle to bring about significant change at this level.

Let us return to the case study of the Campbells to illustrate how these three levels operate in the real world, and the actions that a health or social care worker could take to challenge discrimination.

Activity 16   **Identifying discriminatory practice and taking action**

Allow about 30 minutes

Take your time with this piece of work as it is an opportunity to review the unit and think about putting your learning into practice. The tables that follow represent 'individual' and 'cultural' dimensions of racism. They both have columns headed 'observations' and 'action'. Now you need to re-read both parts of the Lorna case study. As you read, note down any examples of individual or cultural racism in the 'Observation' column. For example, on the first table you might note down the verbal abuse experienced by Lorna at school. On the second table you might include the common belief in the children's home that Black children should be treated in the same way as white. Don't worry if you struggle with deciding which table to put your observations down on, just make a note of them. When you have finished, look back at each of your observations and try to think of an 'action' which you as an individual care worker could take to address each incident or issue you have noted. Try and be creative.

Individual	
Observations	**Actions**
Verbal insults towards Lorna.	Make a verbal challenge, model alternative ways of behaving, tell others how such language/behaviour makes you feel, ask what is meant by such language/behaviour.

Cultural	
Observations	**Actions**
Staff at The Lawns did not recognise the significance for Lorna of having her hair braided.	Act as an advocate for Lorna, by seeking understanding of the significance of cultural practices. Identify appropriate services such as consulting with hairdressers specialising in African Caribbean hair.

Comment   This is a major activity. You may find it took a while to complete and
needed some careful thought. Don't worry, anti-discriminatory practice is
not easy and for most of us involves changing the way in which we see
the world, questioning things we have always taken for granted. I have
given fairly full feedback on this activity to help you along.

Individual	
Observations	**Actions**
Verbal insults towards Lorna e.g. Lorna called a 'Pakki' at school.	Make a verbal challenge, model alternative ways of behaving, tell others how such language/behaviour makes you feel, ask what is meant by such language/behaviour.
Staff failed to acknowledge or address the racism Lorna was experiencing or her need to explore her cultural and racial identity.	Make a verbal challenge, model alternative ways of behaving, tell others how such language/behaviour makes you feel, ask what is meant by such language/behaviour
Lorna was avoided by staff and children in The Lawns.	Raise the issue of cultural needs in a staff group discussion; put the issue on the agenda and share responsibility for tackling it as a group.

Cultural	
Observations	**Actions**
Staff at The Lawns did not recognise the significance for Lorna of having her hair braided.	Act as an advocate for Lorna, by seeking understanding of the significance of cultural practices. Identify appropriate services such as consulting with hairdressers specialising in African Caribbean hair.
Common belief in the children's home was that Lorna's race and culture should be disregarded and she should be treated in the same way as white children. Her cultural need for different hair care was not recognised, as it was seen as comparable to white children having a perm.	Raise the issue of cultural needs in a staff group discussion; put the issue on the agenda and share responsibility for tackling it as a group. Seek support from knowledgeable individuals who have contact with the culture of the service user and argue for resources to meet individual needs.

Lorna's behaviour was quickly labelled as 'aggressive' and 'uncooperative'	Take time to question assumptions in the staff team about the causes of behaviour. Involve the service user in discussions and ensure that issues such as racism are put on the agenda and taken seriously.
As an adult Lorna remained labelled as aggressive, and soon became seen as dangerous.	Challenge and question the use of labels and stereotypes, look for alternative explanations which include a recognition of the impact of racism.
Lorna's parenting was judged without reference to explanations linked to her experiences of racism. Her anger towards social workers who failed to consult her and involve her in decisions about her children's needs was interpreted as evidence of 'dangerous parenting'	Challenge and question the use of labels and stereotypes, look for alternative explanations that include a recognition of the impact of racism.

Key points

- The experience of racism is not about isolated events. It can be a life time's experience of systematic discrimination.
- Taking action to counter racism requires care workers to seek knowledge and critically question the way in which services are provided.
- Although racism is often perpetuated at the level of institutions and the broader culture, for individual care workers opportunities to act to counter racism will tend to arise at the personal, individual level.

Conclusion

This unit has introduced important issues for everybody interested in the provision of high quality care services within communities. You should now have some understanding of the diversity and complexity of the communities in which services are provided, and I hope that Lorna Campbell's story has helped you understand how this 'diversity' translates into very different individual experiences and individual needs. Throughout the unit some challenging terminology has been introduced – culture, stereotypes, prejudice, discrimination and institutional racism. I hope that you will now be able to look out for and recognise these processes in the rest of K100 and also in your own lives. Through Lorna's case study you have seen some of the ways in which members of Black and Minority Ethnic groups experience discriminatory care services. This can result in Black and Minority Ethnic people either being excluded from services or provided with services that fail to fully meet their needs. Legislation places a duty on care workers to combat racism in all its forms, but this is not an easy task.

Discrimination is not unusual – it is the everyday experience of many people. You have spent some time thinking about what care workers can do to combat discrimination, at all levels. The first step for all of us is recognising our own culture and then trying to understand the cultures of those we work with and provide services for. This should enable both providers and receivers of services to recognise the equal value and uniqueness of each person they meet.

Study skills: Tackling the assignment

Now you are half way through Block 3, how are you shaping up to your next assignment? With two block's worth of experience behind you, what have you learned about the writing process? In fact, how has the essay writing gone generally? Have you found it a struggle to get your ideas together and get the writing done? Did it turn your week upside down? Were you a pain to family and friends?

Did reading the first two sections of Chapter 11 of *The Good Study Guide* help? Did you find you could break the essay work into stages, as suggested, and work on them a bit at a time? How will you organise your work on TMA 03? Why not try jotting down a plan of attack now, and then see whether you can stick to it.

Study diary

In fact you could include this reflection on essay writing as part of bringing your study diary up to date.

References

Ahmad, B. (1996) *Black Perspectives in Social Work*, NISW/Venture Press, Birmingham.

Barn, R., Sinclair, R., Ferdinand, D. (eds) (1997a) *Acting on Principle: An examination of race and ethnicity in social services provision for children and families*, BAAF, London.

Barn, R., Sinclair, R., Ferdinand, D. (eds) (1997b) *Understanding Racism and Developing Good Practice*, Organisational and Social Development Consultant (OSDC), Macmillan Press, Hampshire.

Beishon S. *et al.* (1995) *Nursing in a Multi-ethnic NHS*, Policy Studies Institute, London.

Bowlby, J. (1953) *Child Care and the Growth of Love*, (2nd edn. 1965), Penguin, Harmondsworth.

Brah, A. (1993) 'Re-framing Europe: engendered racisms, ethnicities and nationalisms in contemporary Western Europe', *Feminist Review*, No. 45, pp. 9–29.

CCETSW (1995) *Assuring Quality on the Diploma in Social Work*, CCETSW, London.

Culley, L. and Dyson, S. (2001) *Ethnicity and Nursing Practice*, Palgrave, Basingstoke.

Department of Health (1999) *Me, Survive Out There? New arrangements for young people living in and leaving care*, The Stationery Office, London.

Department of Health (2000a) *The Vital Connection: an equalities framework for the NHS working together for quality and equality*, The Stationery Office, London.

Department of Health (2000b) *Excellence not excuses: inspection of services for ethnic minority children and families*, The Stationery Office, London.

Department of Health (2001) *The Children Act Now: Messages from research*, The Stationery Office, London.

Department of Health/Department for Education and Employment (2000) *Guidance on the Education of Children and Young People in Public Care*, The Stationery Office, London.

Dominelli, L. (1988) *Anti-Racist Social Work: A challenge for white practitioners and educators*, (2nd edn 1992), Macmillan, Basingstoke.

Dominelli, L., Lorenz, W., Lorenz Soydan, H. (eds) (2001) *Beyond Racial Divides: Ethnicities in social work practice*, Ashgate/CEDR, Aldershot.

Dwivedi, K. and Varma, V. (1996) '*Meeting the Needs of Ethnic Minority Children*', Jessica Kingsley Publishers, London.

Fook, J. (2001) in Dominelli, L., Lorenz, W., Lorenz Soydan, H. (eds) *Beyond Racial Divides: Ethnicities in social work practice*, Ashgate/CEDR, Aldershot.

Gerrish, K. *et al.* (1996) *Nursing for a Multi-Ethnic society*, Open University Press, Buckingham.

Gilroy, P. (1992) 'The end of racism' in Donald, J. and Rattansi, A., *Race Culture and Difference*, Sage, London.

Grotberg, E. (1995) *A Guide to Promoting the Resilience of Children: Strengthening the human spirit*, Bernard Van Leer Foundation, The Hague, Netherlands.

Inner London Probation Service (1993) *Working with Difference*, ILPS, London.

Jackson, S. (ed.) (2001) *'Nobody Ever Told us that School Mattered'*, BAAF, London, http://www.baaf.org.uk [accessed 9.7.02].

Keating, F. (1993) in ILPS, *Working with Difference*, ILPS, London.

Lambeth Social Services Committee (1981) *Black Children in Care Report*, Lambeth Social Services Department, London.

Marlow, A. and Loveday, B. (eds) (2000) *After Macpherson*, Russell House, Lyme Regis.

Mehra, H. (1996) 'Residential care for ethnic minority children' in Dwivedi, K. and Varma, V. (1996) *Meeting the Needs of Ethnic Minority Children*, Jessica Kingsley Publishers, London.

Moyenda (1995), *Moyenda Project Report 1991–94, Exploring Parenthood*, London.

Owusu-Bempah, J. (1994) 'Race, self identity and social work', *British Journal of Social Work*, Vol. 24, No. 2, pp. 123–36.

Papadopoulos, I. *et al.* (1998) *Transcultural Care: A guide for health care professionals*, Quay Books, Wilts.

Patel, V. and Singh, S. (1998) *Regarding Scotland's Black Children. – Research on the policy and practice of service provision for children from black and minority ethnic communities*, SBWF, Edinburgh.

Rutter, M. (1986) *Maternal Deprivation Reassessed* (2nd edn), Penguin, Harmondsworth.

Rutter, M. (1990) 'Psychosocial resilience and protective mechanisms' in Rolf, J. *et al.* (eds) *Risk and Protective Factors in the Development of Psychopathology*, Cambridge University Press, Cambridge.

Schaffer, H.R. (1992) *Making Decisions About Children*, Backwell, Oxford.

Skellington, R. (1996) *Race in Britain Today*, Sage/Open University Press.

Small, J. (1984) 'The crisis in adoption', *International Journal of Social Psychiatry*, Vol. 30, Nos.1 and 2, Spring.

Thoburn, J. (1988) *Child Placement: Principles and practice*, Community Care Practice Handbooks, Aldershot, Wildwood House.

Thompson, N. (2000) *Anti-discriminatory Practice*, Macmillan, London.

Zeitlin, H. 'Adoption of children from minority groups' in Dwivedi, K. and Varma, V. (1996) *Meeting the Needs of Ethnic Minority Children*, Jessica Kingsley Publishers, London.

Acknowledgements

Grateful acknowledgement is made to the following sources for permission to reproduce material in this book:

Text

pp. 100: Parr, M. (1984) 'Am I black or am I white?' from *It's Bad for your Child to be in Care*, Children's Legal Centre.

Figures

Fig. 2: Papadopoulos, I., Tiki, M. and Taylor, G. (1998) *Transcultural Care: A Guide for Health Care Professionals*, Quay Books, Mark Allen Publishing Ltd; *Fig. 3:* Thompson, N. (1993) *Anti-Discriminatory Practice*, Macmillan Press Ltd, reproduced with permission of Palgrave Macmillan.

Illustrations

p. 64: Steve Eason/Photofusion; *p. 68 (top):* David Trainer/Photofusion; *p. 68 (bottom):* M. Haddad/Photofusion; *p. 73:* Sam Tanner/Photofusion; *p. 78:* Bob Watkins/Photofusion; *p. 85 (right):* Gary Simpson/Photofusion; *p. 85 (left):* Caroline Mardon/Photofusion; *p. 96:* Paul Doyle/Photofusion.

Unit 12
Working with Communities

Prepared for the course team by Pam Foley (new for the 2003 edition)

While you are working on Unit 12, you will need:
- Offprints Book

Contents

Introduction

In Unit 10 we looked at how community health and care services are supposed to respond to individual people's needs and in Unit 11 we examined what communities mean to different groups of people and how communities respond to the health and social needs of differing groups within society. In Unit 12 we expand this a little more and think about how communities, as a whole, can improve health. We are going to look at what we might mean by a 'healthy community' and, at the other extreme, how communities can be so 'unhealthy' that their members run the risk of 'exclusion' from the wider society. We also look at how the health and well-being of people can be improved by social and community-based action and how, increasingly, local people and organisations are working to realise the potential of communities.

Core questions

- What is a 'healthy community'?
- What is social exclusion?
- How might communities be regenerated?
- What makes work within communities effective?

Section 1
Healthy communities

Communities have the potential to make a real impact, for better or worse, on people's health and well-being. Health is fundamentally linked with where people live, their homes, their surroundings and the communities of which they are a part. Let's begin by thinking about what unhealthy communities look like and the effects they might have.

Activity 1   **An unhealthy place to live?**

Allow about 10 minutes   Can you think of a community or neighbourhood that you would describe as unhealthy? What would it look it? Make a few notes of the characteristics of an unhealthy place to live.

Comment   One of the first things you may have thought of is the physical environment – old and decrepit housing, derelict housing estates marked by vandalism and graffiti and streets strewn with rubbish. You might also have thought of certain aspects of quality of life we often hear about, such as crime, and the fear of crime. You may have noted that communities experience marked differences in mortality (rates of death) and morbidity (rates of disease and illness). These include numbers of accidents in and around the home. There is often a lack of places to play or facilities where young people can meet. Some people will experience the effects of racism and discrimination on their health and sense of well-being. Poor educational provision and achievement is usually a feature, too, and there may be high levels of school exclusion and truancy. Overall, the picture of an unhealthy neighbourhood that comes to mind is of a group of people living together, caught up with a series of social, economic and health problems but without the information, skills or resources to protect or promote their health and well-being.

For some adults, who spend most of their day away from their home and its surroundings, their community may play a relatively small part in their lives. But for others, particularly those whose mobility is restricted through poverty, caring responsibilities, age or impairment, the neighbourhood has a significant impact on their lives. (Think, for example, of the lives of Lynne and Arthur Durrant in Block 1.)

The King's Fund is an independent charitable organisation working to improve health in the UK [www.kingsfund.org.uk]

The King's Fund report *Healthy Neighbourhoods* (2001) carried out research into how healthy communities can be developed and achieved. The report began by suggesting some defining characteristics. A healthy neighbourhood, they suggested, is safe, clean, inclusive, confident, creative and connected; and it also has certain characteristics:

- resources: buildings, land, people

- amenities: such as sports and leisure facilities, attractive public spaces

- other positive components: including schools and workplaces

- knowledge: understanding of what is needed and what could work

- potential: assets and capacities that can be developed to improve health

- services: private, public and voluntary bodies already working in the neighbourhood (King's Fund, 2001).

As in Activity 1, when we thought about what made some communities 'healthy' or 'unhealthy', the King's Fund report underlines how communities aren't just about *material* resources or lack of them, (although these are undoubtedly important); they are also about those *human* resources that make up a community, in other words the people who live and work there. (We will be using this list of characteristics again in connection with another activity later in the unit.)

Communities (places and people) are called upon to meet a wide variety of health and social needs and a range of different resources are involved. A neighbourhood that promotes health will be one in which the houses, streets and public spaces are safe, clean and pleasant and where public services are available, accessible, effective and efficient. Healthy communities are also capable of meeting a variety of social needs through the creation or enhancement of places, spaces and buildings and by offering opportunities for relaxation and recreation. Communities can also be a positive force in valuing and respecting diversity and building on local distinctiveness.

Communities can also be a positive force in valuing and respecting diversity

What is particularly noticeable about a community approach to health and well-being is that it encourages workers in health, education and social care, and the organisations they work for, to work together across traditional boundaries. Too often this has not been the case in the past. In the last few years the recognition of the need for more inter-agency and inter-professional working has led to a new approach to policy formation. The recognition that families and sometimes whole communities can suffer from a range of interlinked problems has given rise to an important new concept within government, that of 'social exclusion'.

1.1 Social exclusion: the impact on communities

The concept of 'social exclusion' is one that is relatively new in British political and social debate. The fundamental shift in thinking that underpins this approach is to look at material and social problems as a series of interconnected issues. While a low income is the key factor, 'social exclusion' is a broader concept. Poverty needs to be understood not simply in terms of how little money some people have, but also in the effects this has on several crucial aspects of life. Social exclusion describes how being poor drastically curtails people's ability to participate in the customary life of their society. A child or young person, for example, experiencing social exclusion might be living in poverty *and* experiencing life in a high crime neighbourhood, in poor housing conditions, experiencing higher incidences of accidents and ill health, and attending a low-achieving school. So a social exclusion approach focuses on the links between unemployment, poor work-related skills, educational underachievement, crime, ill health and substandard housing – all of which have a negative impact on people's lives. (Another example might be Jim and Marianne's story as told in Unit 10; this graphically illustrates how combinations of connected circumstances such as ill health, drug misuse and homelessness can lead to people becoming socially excluded.)

In some places whole communities are blighted by these multiple, interlinked problems; often these problems have built up over decades and across generations. Particular groups are particularly vulnerable to becoming socially excluded; these include children and young people in public care, families in no-work households, children and young people who no longer attend school and those who may be additionally disadvantaged by racism and other forms of discrimination. Such disadvantages can, of course, be cumulative. The social exclusion approach is one that maintains that social, health and economic policies can only be effective when these problems are understood and addressed as *interlinked and interactive.*

The Social Exclusion Unit within the Cabinet Office was set up in 1997 specifically to address the issue of social exclusion through interdepartmental work. Government policies of the past were seen as ineffective primarily because they tried to tackle problems one at a time. They tended to become too focused on dealing with social problems rather than preventing them, and were doing things *for* people rather than enabling them to do things for themselves. Intervention had repeatedly failed to prevent a downward spiral of social exclusion despite evidence that early intervention could be effective and, furthermore, policies and practices were unable to reintegrate those who had become excluded. Basic services such as health care and schools were seen to be weakest where they were needed most.

Employment remains the key component in New Labour policies to reduce social exclusion (Social Exclusion Unit, 2001). Yet, as has been pointed out, focusing on work as the main means of reconnecting and reintegrating people depends heavily on full employment opportunities and ultimately fails to address the issue of how those who cannot work can share in rising national prosperity (Piachaud, 1999). However, tackling social exclusion has been made a priority in budget allocation and spending reviews, and the government has committed itself to annual reporting of its anti-poverty strategy (Department of Social Security, 1999). The Social Exclusion Unit, during its first five years, has worked on a range of issues and has produced cross-departmental publications on:

- *Truancy and School Exclusion* (1998)
- *Rough Sleeping* (1998)
- *Teenage Pregnancy* (1999)

- *Bridging the Gap: New opportunities for 16–18-year-olds not in education, employment or training* (1999)

- *Neighbourhood Renewal: A new commitment to neighbourhood renewal* (2001)

- *Consultation Report on Young Runaways* (2001).

The Social Exclusion Unit only covers England. In Scotland, the Scottish Parliament has produced *The Policy Framework for Tackling Poverty and Social Exclusion in Scotland* (2000) which emphasises policies that promote social inclusion and works through its Scottish Social Inclusion Network. The Action Teams focus on three priority areas: excluded young people, inclusive communities and the impact of local anti-poverty action. Social Inclusion Partnerships also work to co-ordinate action at a local level (http://www.scottish.parliament.uk [accessed 6.6.02]). In Wales, tackling social disadvantage is one of the major themes of the Welsh Assembly's *Better Wales* (http://www.wales.gov.uk [accessed 5.6.02]) and it is working through the national programmes 'People in Communities', 'Communities First' and a grant-aided scheme 'Social Disadvantage: Sustainable Communities' (http://www.wales.gov.uk).

Action to tackle social exclusion has three broad goals:

1   To prevent social exclusion by reducing the numbers of those at risk and by compensating for those circumstances which appear to lead to social exclusion.

2   To reintegrate those who are experiencing social exclusion back into society by providing clear paths for those who have lost their jobs or homes or missed out on education.

3   To ensure that public services deliver basic minimum standards – in health, education, employment and tackling crime (Social Exclusion Unit, 2001).

This focus on prevention, reintegration and mainstream services is also backed up by a more open approach to policy-making, which involves listening to the views of people who are affected by social exclusion. (We will be looking at this aspect of work to tackle social exclusion later in the unit.)

1.2 Tackling social exclusion at the local level

Neighbourhood renewal is one of the 'big ideas' in the government's campaign to tackle social exclusion. 'Neighbourhood renewal' or 'regeneration' means, in essence:

- someone in charge at local level

- reorganisation of public services as the main instrument of renewal

- maximum involvement from communities and voluntary and private organisations

- targeted assistance from government (Taylor, 2000).

But even its most committed supporters cannot claim that community development work is new. Community development, an approach to health and social care grounded on developing the skills and capacities of local people, has been around for a while.

'The Peckham Experiment' Preventive health intervention community programmes have been around since the 1920s

The Groundwork movement (another example, but still active) has been working with communities for over 20 years; its 50 trusts across England, Wales and Northern Ireland undertake community-based regeneration work, often in the most deprived communities (Fordham and Lawless, 2002).

In a review of published research into the major area-based regeneration programmes, *Top-down Meets Bottom-up: Neighbourhood management* (Taylor, 2000), researchers for and at the Joseph Rowntree Foundation asked what we have learnt from community work experience so far. They argued that vital to effective neighbourhood renewal is a strong infrastructure of workers and services which spread rather than protect their knowledge, resources, skills and learning (and we will be looking at how this can be done in Section 2). They also emphasised that there will be no sustainable change until communities themselves are given the power and responsibility to take action. Taylor (2000) and colleagues also maintained that the long-term perspective is essential if integrated approaches to social inclusion are to be sustainable. To maximise the involvement of the community, people and organisations need time to change, time to find out what works and time for that work to take effect.

In 2001 the Social Exclusion Unit published a major report on those communities which had, in Tony Blair's words, become 'scarred by unemployment, educational failure and crime' and 'progressively more cut off from the prosperity and opportunities that most of us take for granted' (Social Exclusion Unit, 2001, p. 5).

The national strategy 'A New Commitment to Neighbourhood Renewal' (Social Exclusion Unit, 2001) addresses not just the physical fabric of poor neighbourhoods but also the intrinsic problems of unemployment, crime and poor public services, low-achieving schools, and too few front-line health care workers. The report identifies a combination of those factors that may be familiar to you as establishing and maintaining the gap between poor neighbourhoods and the rest. These factors can include localised pockets of unemployment resulting from the decline of manufacturing industry, rising skills demands affecting new employment prospects, greater numbers of family break-ups resulting in many lone parents and their children living on benefits, the declining popularity of public housing, the increased concentration of people from vulnerable groups and the increasing availability of drugs and the growth of the drug economy (Social Exclusion Unit, 2001).

Poor neighbourhoods have a major impact on the quality of life of all those living within them, particularly vulnerable groups including lone parents, older people, disabled people and Black and Minority Ethnic residents. Local public services can also be put under strain just when people need them most, and if people start to leave the area a destabilised community can mean a deteriorating physical environment and more crime. For children and young people this can be particularly damaging. Children are particularly dependent on their locality – it is the setting for much of their day-to-day lives and the backdrop for much of their learning about life beyond their families. Certain neighbourhoods can also carry a stigma which itself makes it harder for young people who live there to get jobs.

Central to the national strategy to renew poor neighbourhoods are methods which try to involve and empower residents and which encourage partnerships of public, private and voluntary organisations.

> *Communities need to be consulted and listened to, and the most effective interventions are often those where communities are actively involved in their design and delivery, and where possible in the driving seat. Often this applies as much to 'communities of interest' – like black and minority ethnic groups, faith communities, older or younger people, or disabled people – as it does to geographical communities.*
>
> *(Social Exclusion Unit, 2001, p. 9)*

While the extent of existing community involvement and resources will differ between communities, perhaps very widely, the report goes on to detail key issues for all community action programmes which need to:

- identify priority neighbourhoods; those who have the lowest quality of life in terms of joblessness, crime, educational failure, ill health, poor physical environment and housing

- understand how these problems impact on residents; regeneration programmes often fail because they focus on symptoms rather than root causes; for example low employment rates may be linked with other barriers to jobs – low skills, poor transport, lack of childcare

- map the resources going into these neighbourhoods; build on what is already in place and working

- agree on what needs to be done; consult people on what they want and set targets

- implement, monitor and evaluate agreed actions (Social Exclusion Unit, 2001).

If community-based regeneration is to work, it has to be rooted in the needs and aspirations of the people living in the community and a long-term view has to be taken. It is clear that for local people and organisations to work effectively together in these ways there has to be a willingness to change and acquire new ways of working, and there must be a significant level of commitment – these things don't happen overnight. Communities are not homogenous entities; it is unwise to assume that there are common aims and aspirations. It is also the case that community regeneration work will meet a significant level of, perhaps well-founded, apathy, disillusionment and maybe antipathy.

So that you can attempt to appreciate all these different aspects, the next activity asks you to take a look at a real-life project.

Activity 2 **The St Matthew's project**

Allow about 30 minutes Read the extract reproduced in Offprint 17.

Thinking about the five points from the Social Exclusion Unit report listed above and about the arguments you have now read about community work, how have the workers in this project addressed each of these five points through their community project work?

Comment Reading about the project, it's clear how neighbourhoods can struggle to adapt to change and how basic services like health care, in priority neighbourhoods such as this, can become overwhelmed and eroded. The project used a consultation exercise to identify what the local people thought they needed to improve their quality of life and this turned out to be somewhere safe for children to play and somewhere women could unwind. It was interesting that people took a broad view of the factors affecting their health and well-being and displayed a sophisticated understanding, focusing not on symptoms but on root causes; and this was reflected in the use of the community rooms by health care practitioners, lawyers, police officers and workers addressing domestic violence. This inter-agency work is being evaluated by an academic department. Residents and paid and voluntary workers are tackling their neighbourhood's economic regeneration and focusing on children and young people's support, and community safety. The overall project was built upon considerable local resources already in place and it is run, it appears, by professional and managerial staff and a local councillor.

National and local policies and legislative changes have considerable impact on the structure and resourcing of care provision in the UK. It's important to see how health, social care and educational policies shape the kinds of actions taken, and services provided, within communities. In the next section we will take a closer look at some examples of community-based work taking place today; we will use as an example community-orientated resources for children and young people.

Key points

- The resources of communities, both material and human, can have a considerable impact on the quality of life of those people, particularly the vulnerable people, who live within them.

- The concept of social exclusion, with its focus on the interlinked and interactive nature of health and social problems, has the potential to make a real difference to the effectiveness of health and social care services.

- If community development work can accurately reflect local aspirations and needs and involve local people, it can, in the long term, make a real difference to people's lives.

Section 2
Children, young people and their communities

What does 'your community' mean to a child or young person? Children and young people may experience their communities very differently.

Activity 3   **Communities then and now**

Allow about 5 minutes   Think for a few minutes about how you and other children and young people were part of your local community when you were a child. What has changed for the children and young people in your community today?

Comment   Clearly it depended then, as now, on where you lived but children and young people have become less visible in many communities. In the past children and young people 'owned' the streets and communal spaces around their homes in ways that are impossible now. In today's traffic-filled streets it's not easy for children to go out to play with friends, and parents are too anxious to let them go out and about on their own. The visibility of children and young people within their communities, so much a part of life for previous generations, is often no longer there. Fears of traffic and 'stranger danger' have effectively eradicated children's street culture – the games and street gangs that were a part of life for previous generations.

Yet while many children and young people, perhaps most, may have lost access to the streets in which they live, many of them, of all classes, travel (including abroad) further afield than ever. Changes within the home have influenced this too; families have shrunk in size and better quality housing and more space mean children may not want to spend time outdoors. They can often usually connect with each other and engage with the outside world through their telephones, televisions and computers. And in some ways children now have alternative spaces in which they seem quite at home – leisure centres and clubs – and children and young people seem to play equal roles as consumers, occupying the shopping streets and malls, with and without adults.

2.1 'The community' – what's in it for us?

Activity 4

Allow about 30 minutes

What's in the community for children and young people?

Do you recall the King's Fund report *Healthy Neighbourhoods* that we looked at earlier in this unit? It listed six characteristics of a healthy community. Thinking about where you live (and using any resources you have easily to hand such as a local telephone directory) use the table below to make some notes on the kinds of organisations and people who work for a healthy community for children and young people in your locality. The first one is filled in to give you an idea of what we're looking for.

Resources – buildings, land, people	Community hall, health centre, church, park Doctors, teachers, childcare workers
Amenities – sports/leisure facilities, attractive public spaces	
Components – schools, workplaces, etc.	
Knowledge – who might know what's needed and what works?	
Potential – assets/capabilities that could be developed	
Services – public, private and voluntary	

Comment

What is noticeable, when you think about it, is that there is a great variety of people and agencies involved in contributing to a healthy community for children and young people – central government, local government, health authorities, voluntary agencies, health and social care charities, health and social care professionals, childcare, leisure and play workers. Unavoidably, perhaps, some of this work will overlap, while significant gaps in provision will remain unaddressed. It's also noticeable that while some communities can offer many, perhaps most, of these resources, there will be some communities, maybe rural or economically disadvantaged, that cannot.

Many people in the wider community can contribute to a healthy community for children and young people

Your **resources** may have included a community hall of some sort, probably a health centre and a church. These sorts of structures will support the development and provision of services which will affect the physical and emotional health of children and young people. Other resources will be the people working in the community with children and young people who will all contribute to their health and well-being: you might have noted down those concerned primarily with health care, such as doctors, health visitors, dentists and chemists; or those working in educational and care settings – teachers, playground supervisors, caterers or social care workers and foster parents caring for children whose parents cannot, or those who provide childcare such as childminders, playgroup and after-school workers. There may also be self-help groups and voluntary groups such as a 'young carers' group'.

Children and young people can be a resource for their community

Amenities will be widely distributed and determined by factors such as whether you live in a city, town or the country; these amenities will determine what health care is available and how proactive the community can be in forging social support and contact. Local transport may have a major impact on how much local children and young people have access to amenities. Your local children may be lucky enough to have a leisure centre, sports club, library, toy library or swimming pool nearby. For older children and young people there may be an internet café – a 'virtual community' of internet websites, e-mails and chat rooms. Some communities have resources available only on certain days – such as a mobile library. There may be an arts related project – a theatre group or a band. Directly, through raising levels of fitness and/or increasing levels of interaction, these amenities can influence local residents' health and well-being.

Leading by example?

Components will include schools, maybe colleges. Schools have an important contribution to make to physical and emotional health including the provision of knowledge and skills that relate to health care and health behaviour. They can also lead by example. The National Healthy School Standard provides accreditation for local education and health partnerships known as Local Healthy Schools Programmes. Health in schools needs to encompass the whole school culture and involve children, parents and the wider community. Most schools today also work collaboratively with external agencies such as social service departments, health professionals, the police and voluntary organisations. Tackling equality issues, addressing bullying, encouraging physical exercise – such as walking to school – and making playgrounds nice places to spend time in are all ways schools can contribute to health and well-being.

Concerns about safety may make outsiders feel unwelcome

Knowledge and **potential** to be developed to support health are more difficult to list, not least because they are quite difficult to see. Experienced community workers will have considerable expertise and influence. Professionals such as health and social care workers, will have considerable potential to influence the health outcomes of the population they work with. They can also help by spreading knowledge of local user support groups. There may be some 'ordinary' people who have the skills needed to get things changed. A community's response will depend upon the willingness of people to organise and run things for themselves. The capacity of a neighbourhood to 'network' seems important, too – how do communities spread information? And did you spot any untapped potential in your neighbourhood? Maybe there is a gaping hole that you see in your community provision – perhaps it's crying out for an after-school club.

Looking at local **services** – for younger children there may be playgroups, childminders, after-school clubs, postnatal support groups and maybe a toy library. Childcare provision, however, remains patchy; currently (2002) the Daycare Trust have established that there is still only one childcare place for every 6.9 children under the age of eight and British parents pay the highest childcare bills in Europe (Land, 2002). You may have included some voluntary agencies such as Home Start, a service run by volunteers for families with young children experiencing difficulties. Some of the local services may be connected with national programmes such as Sure Start (more of which later).

As we look at what is provided locally, we begin to see just how it is that communities can have a positive or negative impact on lives. And it is also possible to see how communities are constrained by their commitment to meet a range of sometimes conflicting needs. Thinking about children and young people and their communities, it becomes clear that some of their needs will, at times, come into conflict with the wishes and needs of other groups in the community. Issues connected with 'public space' might help explain what I mean.

For children, play is a vital part of their lives but it is frequently marginalised in both the planning and budgeting of local facilities. Play has a low status and so play provision has a low priority and play workers are not recognised as skilled workers. However, since play makes an important contribution to children's physical, emotional and social well-being, it makes an essential contribution to the quality of children's lives and thereby to the communities they live in (Mental Health Foundation, 1999).

Play remains fundamental to children's health and well-being.

The Children's Play Council (CPC) (funded by both the Department for Culture, Media and Sport and the DfES) is looking at how a *play perspective* can and should inform public policy and provision. The term *play perspective* is used here to indicate an emphasis on children's appetite for life, their need for freedom and choice and their ability to learn through self-motivation. The CPC also suggests that every child is *entitled* to space and time to play. Playwork takes a positive attitude to activities often seen as problematic in children – risk taking, conflict, challenging behaviours – not seeing them as things to be eliminated but as the building blocks of social and emotional development. Play can offer children choices, respect their abilities, foster their self-esteem and, most distinctively, encourage exploration and testing of boundaries (Gill, 2000). It makes a significant contribution to children's health, learning and social and emotional development, thereby strengthening families and communities. As children's lives have become more constrained, physically and socially, and more pressurised, intellectually and emotionally, there is, for many, a growing realisation that play, and the space to play, can be a positive force in children and young people's lives.

However children, particularly older children and young people, are often made to feel uncomfortable in those public spaces that we so often think of in relation to communities – around streets, shops and parks. When they are 'hanging around' it's often assumed they are up to no good and that their parents probably don't know where they are.

They may feel they are being moved from one public space to another, frequently coming into conflict with other sections of the community and never feeling they have a space of their own. Controversial plans to introduce local curfews for under 16s are just one expression of how the impression can be given – both to communities and to children and young people themselves – that children and young people are disliked and even dangerous.

Here children and young people's interests come up against strong social trends as recent debates around 'hypermobility' have shown. While some adults clock up ever-increasing car mileage travelling to and from work or to see family and friends, children and young people have become less mobile, the extent of traffic making children and parents unwilling or unable to walk or cycle to school or friends' houses. Changes to make communities more child friendly would involve, for example, many more traffic calming measures, and streets designed to encourage easy walking and cycling to shops, schools and town centres.

From the 'Reclaim the Streets' campaign in Sheffield

Central government has responded to the demand for financial support for local public space initiatives such as introducing European style 'home zones', safe routes and urban park programmes. Policy changes, funding and practical action may see children having improved access to and use of their environment. But the trends against walking and cycling, against children's independent mobility, still appear strongly set in the opposite direction.

Maybe we need to prioritise making the communities in which we live safer and more welcoming for children and young people. The Mental Health Foundation Report *Bright Futures: Promoting children and young people's mental health* (1999) summarised the main existing research evidence and suggested that as many as one in five children and young people are suffering from mental health problems such as eating disorders, self-harm, emotional distress or depression. The report goes on to link the development of 'emotional literacy' with the relationship of children and young people to their communities.

> *Fear of abuse and fears about road safety together with a reduction in neighbour and extended family responsibility for the community's children is increasing the number of children who are unpractised in making and consolidating friendships, dealing with conflict, the taking of risks and team games – all key components in the development of emotional literacy.*
>
> (The Mental Health Foundation, 1999, p.15)

So, children and young people look to their communities to meet a range of physical, emotional, social and intellectual needs; they also need communities of which they can feel a part. Families need to be able to draw upon a range of resources to meet the needs of children and young people and nearly all families will be looking to their communities to provide certain resources. Where this becomes particularly critical is in relation to the community's vulnerable children.

2.2 Vulnerable children in the community

While all children and young people need good quality core public services such as health and education, safe places to play, decent housing, leisure opportunities and an inclusive community free of crime, anti-social behaviour and racial harassment, some will have particular needs. While the majority of children and young people are well cared for, there are vulnerable children and young people in every community. This vulnerability may be due to:

* poverty and social exclusion

* they (or their parents) being disabled

* diminished parenting capacity – some parents are isolated or inexperienced, or caught up with alcoholism or drug misuse, physical or mental illness

* parental conflict or violence

* living away from their families, excluded from school or with special educational needs.

The Children Act (1989) defines 'children in need' in broad and developmental terms as children unlikely to achieve or maintain a reasonable standard of health and development without services, whose health and development will be significantly impaired without services or who are disabled. In order to respond to the needs and aspirations of children in need, an assessment framework (see Figure 1) has been developed that enables an increased understanding of what is happening to a child in relation to their parents and the wider context of family and community (Department of Health, 2000). The interaction of three domains – the child's developmental needs, the parenting capacity and the family and environmental factors – will have a direct impact on the current and long-term well-being of a child.

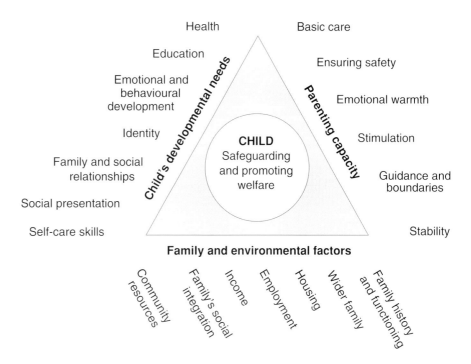

Figure 1
Framework assessment triangle (from DoH, DfEE and HO, 2000)

The use of the assessment framework reflects an increasing willingness among health and social care workers to consider the wider circumstances in which families are bringing up children and the impact of environment factors. Clear and measured differences are apparent in the health and education of children growing up in areas of deprivation. This has an impact both on adults' ability to parent and on children themselves, through the standards of schools available to them, the subculture of peer groups with whom they relate and the community facilities they lack (Rose, 2000).

Child poverty

The widening income gap through the 1980s and 1990s has resulted in strikingly diverse life chances for different groups of British children. Although among the world's richest nations, with 19.8 per cent of children living in poverty, the UK ranks 20th out of 23 in the child poverty league.

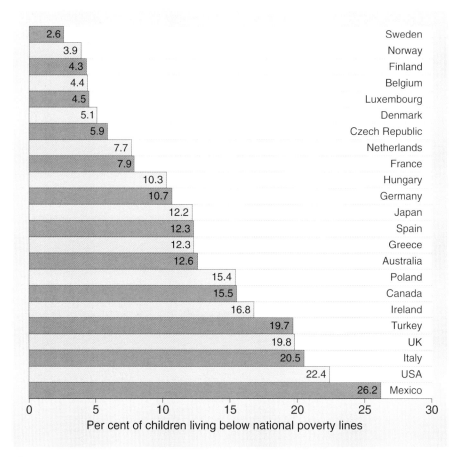

Figure 2
The child poverty league (the figure shows the percentage of children living in 'relative'
poverty, defined as households with income below 50 per cent of the national median)

Activity 5 Child poverty in the UK

Allow about 15 minutes   Clearly, child poverty in the UK is a major issue. Make some brief notes on the range of effects poverty might have on children and young people.

Comment   Children growing up poor are more likely to have learning difficulties, to drop out of school, to use drugs, to commit crimes, to be unemployed, to become pregnant at an early age, and to go on to live lives that involve higher levels of morbidity and mortality; these effects are often perpetuated into succeeding generations (UNICEF, 2000). Child poverty, then, presents governments and societies of the developed world with a test of their ability to address its most deeply rooted health and social problems.

The impact of child poverty is far reaching, as this report makes clear:

> *Whether measured by physical and mental development, health and survival rates, educational achievement or job prospects, incomes or life expectancies, those who spend their childhood in poverty of income and expectation are at a marked and measurable disadvantage.*

> *(UNICEF, 2000, p. 3)*

There exist many causes of child poverty – unemployment and its distribution, wage inequality, state support for those without work and for the low paid, lone parenthood – and while each of these is important, none is pre-eminent (UNICEF, 2000). The UNICEF report looked at countries that have, despite economic recession and social change, held their child poverty rates at a steady 5 per cent for the last 20 years. The Nordic countries, Denmark, Finland, Norway and Sweden, have shown a long-term commitment to policies that help people – particularly women – into paid work. This is supported by high social expenditure funded by tax revenues and other sources. These social policies, rather than targeting resources towards particular groups, cover the entire population.

One key element of these socio-economic policies has been a focus on gender equality, specifically enabling work and parenting combinations that support a more equal share of responsibility for childcare between parents. Extensive parental leave, including paternity leave and entitlement to day care supports a high female workforce participation (averaging over 70 per cent). There is a corresponding strong link between high female employment and low rates of child poverty. It is clear that this consistent, widespread family support, through social and economic policies, is firmly rooted in Nordic culture. In Norway, for example, the interests and welfare of children and young people have been promoted by a Children's Ombudsperson, the world's first, since 1981. He or she has unrestricted access to private and public institutions for children. There is also a Ministry of Children and Family Affairs. This ministry is able to draw together and address collectively certain key issues for children and families (which in the UK are addressed by different ministries) including family policy, family law, gender inequality, day-care facilities, child and adolescent welfare, adoption, and opportunities for children and young people to take part in decision making in society.

In the UK poverty remains the greatest single threat to the health and well-being of children and young people; here, child poverty trebled between 1979 and 1995 (Social Exclusion Unit, 2001).

Activity 6	**Counting the cost**
Allow about 15 minutes	With *Counting the Cost of Child Poverty* (2000) Barnardo's used a published report and a press campaign to illustrate vividly the grim effects of early deprivation on young lives.

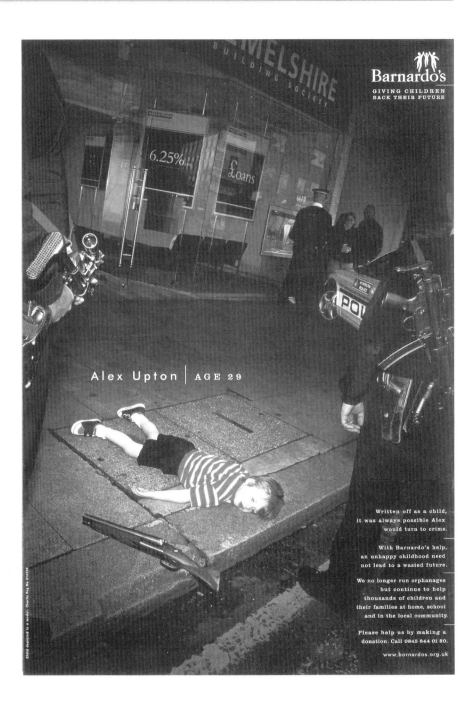

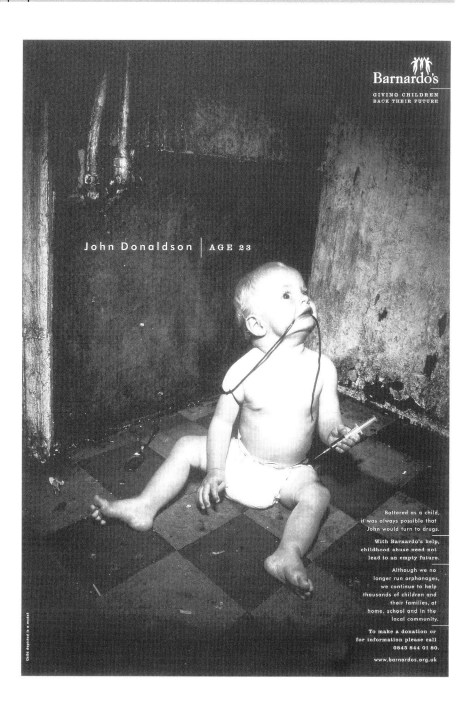

What messages do you read in these advertisements?

Comment | Like me, you may have found these images particularly disturbing. Perhaps it's connected with seeing children in these bleak and frightening settings. Perhaps it's to do with the way some children's lives seem to be blighted from the start. What this campaign communicated, very effectively I thought, is that the failure to help at key stages in the lives of children and young people leads to a train of events which exact huge costs for that individual. Here is the human cost of families and/or the state failing to protect and provide for children.

In 1999 a new Labour government, faced with the level of child poverty in Britain more than twice as high as in France or the Netherlands and five times higher than in Norway or Sweden (UNICEF, 2000) announced the eradication of child poverty as a goal for the year 2020 (Blair, 1999). New Labour policies since 1997 have raised family incomes in real terms through the working families tax credit, an increase in child benefit, and the child credit to be introduced into the tax system in 2003.

It remains to be seen whether the government will achieve its objectives for substantial reductions in child poverty, although it is increasingly clear that further changes to government policies which support families and children are likely to be necessary (Land, 2002).

The seriousness of the pledge is underlined by the government's willingness to measure progress using a wide range of social indices including incomes, health, housing, crime, lone parenthood, teenage pregnancy and educational achievement. These are to be co-ordinated by the Cabinet Committee on Children and Young People's Services focusing on policies to prevent poverty and underachievement among children and young people, co-ordinating and monitoring the effectiveness of service delivery, and working with the voluntary sector to build a new alliance for children. The Committee will be supported by a new cross-departmental Children and Young People's Unit (http://www.cypu.gov.uk). In its strategy document 'Tomorrow's Future: Building a strategy for children and young people' (2001) the government speaking directly to children and young people described the position thus:

> *The Government has committed itself to improve services and radically create plans and opportunities that put children and young people at the very heart of Government to ensure all children and young people have the best chance in life to achieve their full potential. We recognise that past governments have not listened to children and young people or, when they have, they have heard only what they wanted to hear. As a result we have failed some of our children who have not known where to go for help or have found services have not helped them.*

> *(CYPU, 2001, p. 1)*

Central government support for children and young people is currently built around three key programmes:

- Sure Start programmes aim to reach a third of children under four years of age who live in poverty and to promote the health and well-being of young children so they are able to flourish when they reach school (http://www.surestart.gov.uk [accessed 10.1.02]).

- The Children's Fund of £450 million over 2001–04 is designed to tackle poverty and disadvantage among children aged five to 13 and their families. Most of this money will support programmes in local areas to work with children of primary school age and their families at risk of disadvantage.

- 'Connexions', launched in April 2001, works with all young people through individual personal advisers and will address, as a priority, those young people living in poor neighbourhoods and who face particular obstacles in their teenage years (http://www.connexions.gov.uk [accessed 5.6.02]).

We will now look more closely at one of these forms of family support, a nationally funded and co-ordinated, community-based programme for children, young people and their families, Sure Start.

Sure Start

Sure Start is the key intervention programme in the government's drive to tackle child poverty and social exclusion in England and Wales. (Following the 'first wave' of Sure Start programmes in England and Wales in 1999, a Sure Start Scotland programme was introduced in 1999, and one in Northern Ireland in 2000). Sure Start programmes, 500 of them by 2004, are concentrated in communities where a high proportion of children live in poverty and they aim to improve the health and well-being of families before and after the birth of children. Programmes work with parents-to-be, and with parents and children to promote the physical, intellectual and social development of children aged 0–3 years through family support, health services and early learning.

Sure Start programmes include a number of core, often pre-existing, services: outreach and home visiting, support for families and parents, good quality play, learning and childcare experiences for children, primary and community health care (including advice about family health and child health and development) and support for children and parents with special needs (including access to specialised services) (http://www.surestart.gov.uk [accessed 31.7.02]).

For the national director of the Sure Start programme, the success or otherwise of Sure Start depends on the ways communities and services work together:

> *Sure Start is about community capacity, about agencies working together, about adding value, about high quality relevant services. But most importantly, Sure Start is about better outcomes for children.*
>
> *(Eisenstadt, 2000)*

While working in many different communities, all Sure Start programmes are expected to work from a set of shared principles. Sure Start services must:

- co-ordinate, streamline and add value to existing services in the Sure Start area

- involve parents, grandparents and other carers in ways that build on their existing strengths

- avoid stigma by ensuring that all local families are able to use Sure Start services

- ensure lasting support by linking Sure Start to services for older children

- be culturally appropriate and sensitive to particular needs

- promote the participation of all local families in the design and working of the programme (http://www.surestart.gov.uk).

While the programmes will only reach some of the UK's children under four years of age, Sure Start also aims to influence mainstream services that affect the lives of all the young children living in poverty. Under the terms of the programme, each programme or project has to be planned and run by a partnership involving statutory and voluntary agencies and parents' representatives. Parents should have a key role in decisions about how the money is spent and how the programme is to be evaluated.

> *Michelle Wheatcroft and Bailey, her 8-month old baby son, found they were unexpectedly welcome when they moved into a council house on the Parson Cross estate in Sheffield. Aside from the usual information about her tenancy, staff at the local housing office made a point of telling her about the services for parents with young children available through Sure Start. A few days later, one of the first letters through the front door of her new home was a bright orange greetings card (with decorative nappy-pin border) from the local programme. With it came a welcome pack highlighting a growing list of parent and child activities. 'I was worried this area was rubbish and that there'd be nothing to do,' says Michelle.*

'Sure Start' gets you out of the house to do things and although it's for the children, it's for the mums as well. It's really good they've started it.

From Upstart (2000) p. 6 The newsletter for everyone in Sure Start

Activity 7   Evaluating Sure Start

Allow about 20 minutes   All Sure Start programmes have these four key objectives:

- Improving social and emotional development – in particular by supporting early bonding between parents and their children, helping families function and enabling early identification and support of children with emotional and behavioural difficulties.

- Improving health – in particular by supporting parents in caring for their children to promote healthy development before and after birth.

- Improving children's ability to learn – in particular by providing high quality environments and childcare that promote early learning and provide stimulating and enjoyable play, improve language skills and ensure early identification of children with special needs.

- Strengthening families and communities – in particular by involving families in building the community's capacity to sustain the programme and create pathways out of social exclusion.

With these four objectives in mind, how might someone like Michelle and her baby, Bailey, benefit from a Sure Start programme?

Comment   Michelle and Bailey have already benefited from the social network that has been set in motion on the Parson Cross estate, and Michelle seems to have appreciated being 'welcomed' in this way. Contact with other local parents may help with practical problems or even any relationship or behavioural difficulties that may arise. Michelle may also benefit from the way Sure Start programmes are built around multi-agency working – they aim to work across traditional boundaries – and this seems to have already worked for Michelle who first heard about Sure Start from her local housing office. Both Michelle and Bailey could feel the benefits of some increased level of support and there should be people to go to if things begin to go wrong. They should also be able to find a local playgroup that has been refurbished through extra funding and provides quality childcare. Michelle has said she also liked being encouraged to 'get out of the house'. Networks such as these may be able to erode some level of social exclusion and begin to rebuild and strengthen communities.

Of course, with an essentially preventive service such as Sure Start, any meaningful assessment of how successful this programme has been, and how effectively the large sums of public money involved have been spent, will need long-term and wide-ranging evaluation. This evaluation will also have to establish ways of finding out who didn't like what Sure Start had to offer, and whose needs and wants were not met by the programme. Ultimately programmes such as Sure Start aim to alter the focus of services from remedial work to preventive work. They seek to engage the wider community and the wider community's resources to become part of the solution for a parent or parents struggling to bring up children in adverse circumstances. You will have your own views about these kinds of programmes. Maybe you are questioning how much 'top down' solutions such as these can really work. Perhaps you think that it doesn't actually matter where the help comes from, as long as there are more resources where it matters. Maybe you think this looks like another in a long line of middle class initiatives in which working class families are monitored and taught how to be better parents. It may seem to you a good example of a government actually putting 'its money where its mouth is', trying to establish a preventive programme which will help children who have a difficult start to life. Or you may be wondering how effective such programmes can hope to be against the backdrop of mainstream social services stretched beyond their capacities. The success or otherwise of Sure Start remains to be seen.

2.3 Community action for children and young people

So what does community action mean to the lives of children and young people and how can children and young people become involved in the planning and carrying out of community action?

Activity 8   **Longbenton Lads**

Allow about 40 minutes   In the offprint section, please read the extract 'Longbenton Lads' about a
    health and fitness group set up by some young men in the North East.

- Would you describe this as 'top-down' or 'grass-roots' action?
- What is distinctive about community-led action such as this?
- What makes community action like this likely to succeed?

Comment   This is clearly 'grass-roots' action by a group of young men and youth workers, and their project highlights the causes and effects of stressful times for young people, particularly young men. The project did not shy away from some of the most deep-seated and troubling aspects of young lives, including widespread drug use, suicide and depression, and the young men were able to find ways to respond to emotional distress that they recognised among themselves as well as among their contemporaries. What is distinctive here is the way the young men involved had a firm grasp of the importance of interlinked aspects of health – physical, social and emotional. Their willingness to think about and respond to the health and well-being of themselves and of those around them meant that the Men's Health Day was clearly a success. The project also enabled those involved to use and acquire skills such as effective gathering of evidence, fundraising, planning, public speaking and evaluation and it is such skills that will improve their likelihood of success in the future. This is a good example of people doing things for themselves (with a little well timed and well judged support from youth workers) and for this reason, too, it seems more likely to have a lasting impact. Most striking to me, however, was the feeling that the young men involved were, through the project, able to make more sense of their lives and had perhaps begun to feel a little more in touch and in control; maybe a little less 'socially excluded' perhaps?

This activity, hopefully, has explored, using a real example, some of the strengths of community-based action that we discussed earlier in the topic. In the final section we will look at another essential ingredient, user participation.

Key points

- Poverty remains the single most important factor determining the life chances of children and young people.

- Communities contain a variety of groups; sometimes the needs and wishes of these groups will come into conflict.

- Community action may be 'top down' or 'bottom up' but all community-orientated approaches aim to enable individuals and groups to define and meet their own health and social care needs.

Section 3
'Changing things where I live'

So far in this unit we have looked at the characteristics of a healthy neighbourhood in some detail and at why and how local people need to be involved and influential in all forms of community action. In this final section of the unit we will be looking at ways people participate in community-based action. Again we will retain the perspective of children and young people because they are some of the more difficult groups to involve and yet they can be effective partners for change within their communities. And the principles of participation we talk about here would, it could be argued, apply to many other people within the community.

3.1 Taking part

There are two separate but linked outcomes of the involvement of children and young people in decision making. First, participation has the potential to change, for the better, the lives of children and young people today. Consultative processes about policies, practices and services can have a significant impact on both the people (police officers, teachers, doctors, social workers and others) and places which shape their lives. Second, the process of participation is an end in itself – it builds capacities and increases levels of self-confidence and self-esteem. Children and young people talk about improved mutual respect and a greater feeling of inclusion and partnership; in other words, children and young people feel less 'socially excluded'. It is also a process of socialisation because, through participation, children and young people learn that just as they have a voice, so do others and that differing views demand the same respect for all. Children and young people may also be empowered to assume their roles as citizens through gaining knowledge about decision-making structures.

The United Nations Convention on the Rights of the Child (UNCRC) emphasises the need to seek the child's opinion and stresses that proper account should be taken of the views, opinions and aspirations of all children. A group called 'Article 12' has been set up by some children and young people, taking its name from Article 12 of the UNCRC which says that all children and young people have the right to express their views and to have them taken seriously. It is a children's rights organisation set up in 1994 to promote children's rights, to voice their views and have their views taken seriously whenever decisions are made which affect their lives. With their report *Respect*, the children and young people of Article 12 carried out a survey into the impact of Article 12 and children's and young people's role in decision making across the UK. They asked questions such as whether the child or young person had ever heard of Article 12 of the UNCRC, whether they were consulted about their views in their family and whether their school respected their views. They asked whether children and young people were consulted when decisions were made in their neighbourhood; the majority of those they asked said it had never been possible for them to express their views.

'Never – I think children never have a chance to make decisions in the community. The councils are forever giving the go-ahead without consulting children.' (14-year-old girl)

The Article 12 researchers went on to ask 'What could be done to make sure children and young people's views are taken seriously?':

'Never – adults like it as it is and don't want to make any changes.' (8-year-old girl)

'Never – people from the council don't come to see us because they don't think we're old enough.' (15-year-old boy)

'Tell councils to ask the whole public including children and young people about decisions and take those into consideration.'(13-year-old girl)

'I think that the older people should listen more to young people because kids these days have strong views as it's a different way of life.' (16-year-old girl living in a children's home)

'Have child representatives in the government.'(16-year-old girl)

At the end of the report the children and young people who had carried out the interviews and written up the research had some suggestions for local communities:

*   We could have a child and young person's council to help decide on local things concerning young people.

*   There could be a young person who can link with the local MP so that children's views can be taken into account.

*   If there are changes to be made, consult the young people of the community as well as the adults.

*   If there are going to be things done in the local community for young people, for example having youth clubs or playgrounds built, then ask the young people how they want it made.

*   There are many local community groups, but have some that include young people in them.

*   Let young people have a say about what kind of shops or entertainment activities are made so that everyone is happy (www.article12.com [accessed 31.7.02]).

Activity 9   **Taking part**

Allow about 20 minutes

Think about ways to involve children and young people more in decision making in the community:

*   What is your initial reaction to the idea of involving children and young people in decision making in the community?

*   What may be the possible benefits, and possible problems?

*   Can you think of any ways in which their participation in community decision making could be supported and which groups of children and young people might have particular difficulty in participating?

Comment

Participation like this needs to be *built into* the ways in which communities work. It needs to be part of an institution's or agency's values and to be part of planning, delivery, resourcing and evaluation of service provision. This means a certain level of openness and honesty; occasionally it is not appropriate to involve children and young people in decision making, sometimes expectations will not be met and there are practical and legal boundaries to be considered. Feedback to everyone who contributed and participated must be timely and clear. Staff may need further training and support to engage effectively with children and young people's participation.

Children and young people can contribute suggestions and complaints in many ways. It's about thinking in new ways as much as anything. Children and young people can gather information on which decisions are made – carrying out evaluative surveys with other children and young people on existing and planned services and gaps in provision. They may need initial help in deciding what questions to ask, how to listen and record and how to get background information. Children and young people can also become involved through more formal consultative processes, such as the Young People's Advisory Forum which advises the Minister for Young People and Children and Young People's Unit (http://www.cypu.gov.uk [accessed 25.7.02]). A consultative process might mean a large or small group, it might use drama, games, drawings or other forms of activities. Communication with and empowerment of children and young people would need to become a greater part of staff training programmes. Children and young people can also become involved in selecting the people who will work for and with them. Panels of young people have been involved in the selection of people working for the 'Connexions' service (http://www.connexions.gov.uk [accessed 5.6.02]).

With thought, children and young people can become members of adult-led advisory and decision-making bodies. It's important to remember that more than one approach may be necessary; it's about selecting those methods most effective and relevant to the particular issue.

There will be a number of children and young people whose voices are marginalised. These will include very young children, disabled children, children and young people living away from home, children from Minority Ethnic backgrounds, children from rural areas or disadvantaged neighbourhoods, children and young people excluded from school, young people in the youth justice system, refugees, traveller children and children with special needs.

> Save the Children Fund and The Children's Society undertook some consultation work with children aged 2–4 years for the Greater London Authority. The children were asked for their perceptions of life in London and were taken for a 'sensory walk', and encouraged to talk about what they saw, smelt, touched, tasted and heard as they walked. Some of the children took photographs, other drew pictures which showed how London streets looked from their perspective. Their comments on noise, litter, safety and amenities are being fed into the GLA strategy.
>
> *(http://www.cypu.gov.uk [accessed 31.7.02])*

Training and support will be needed for advocacy and supporting adults seeking to help these children and young people have a voice. For young children this may involve innovative methods including combinations of visual and verbal communication, such as children's own photographs, tours and maps (Clark and Moss, 2001) and for older children this may mean information which is accessible and intelligible. You may need to plan to overcome physical access problems, or present in ways other than written text. Some children will have had bad experiences of government services and agencies. Special consideration, perhaps through organisations with expertise in reaching out to disengaged children, needs to be given to include these children and young people.

It's also essential that children and young people understand from the start how the information and views they share will be used. Their contribution should always be responded to and acknowledged. Children and young people may need 'up-skilling' in order to participate meaningfully and to avoid tokenism or a 'tick box' approach.

This will, of course, be a learning process for everyone involved. The success, or otherwise, of differing methods to enable children and young people to express their views and to maximise the impact of their contribution will need to be continually assessed.

There is a long way to go and it will be a gradual process. Adult and organisational perspectives continue to dominate and may take a long time to change. But there appears to be a discernible shift towards acting upon the idea that children and young people can and should have a real say in the policies and services that affect them. Their contribution to, and benefit from, their communities will depend on them being heard and valued and being able to make a difference.

3.2 At what age does one become a citizen?

We spend the first four years of our lives learning to walk and talk, then we are put in school and told to sit down and be quiet ... not for long though. It seems that with Citizenship about to become part of our curriculum, the students are the ones who will be enforcing change in schools.

(Malik, 2001, p. 10)

A relatively new development, which might make a difference both to participation and to communities, is the introduction of 'citizenship' into both primary and secondary schools. Citizenship will be introduced into the National Curriculum in secondary schools from September 2002 promoting political literacy, social and moral responsibility and community involvement. Citizenship education has three strands:

- social and moral responsibility: young people learning self-confidence and socially and morally responsible behaviour

- community involvement: children and young people learning to become involved in the life and concerns of their neighbourhood and communities including learning through community involvement and service

- political literacy: learning about the institutions, issues and practices of our democracy and how citizens can make themselves effective in public life, locally, regionally and nationally through skills and values as well as knowledge (DfES, http://www.dfes.gov.uk/ [accessed 6.6.02]).

Young people were involved in the planning and piloting of the DfES Citizenship website.

The Citizenship Team ran two workshops with young people to look at what they would like to see on the website. The workshops were arranged as part of the South London and North London 'Your Turn' (local partnership) events involving groups of 11–15-year-olds. Here Eleanor, one of the young people involved, talks about 'citizenship', how she participated in taking this idea forward and how she thinks this might change things for young people today.

From September 2002, every secondary school-aged child in the country will have Citizenship lessons added to their already crammed timetables. The government, sensibly, wanted feedback from the people this would affect, and throughout 2000 several groups of students were involved in different ways. I was asked to participate in one such programme called 'Your Turn' which aims to teach young people the value of citizenship in ways that schools cannot.

Thirty young people took part, three from each of ten schools, participating in a number of group discussions, tours and visits. Those chosen were those schools dubbed the country's 'future leaders'. Arguably, this is already presuming quite a lot, for we know that it was for this reason that we had been picked. In my opinion, it would have made more sense and the feedback given would have represented a fairer cross section of society, if children of different abilities had been chosen.

The whole purpose of the workshops was to encourage us to be 'good' citizens and to understand the duties and responsibilities that come with living in a community. We participated in eight programme days (instead of school) and we looked at education, governance (who runs your city?), economy, health, the criminal justice system and image and culture.

At different points we visited Price Waterhouse Coopers, the Houses of Parliament, Guy's Hospital, the GLA, the Department of Culture, Media and Sport, South Bank Technopark, and Tower Bridge Magistrates' Court. At each venue we had talks and group discussions and activities, exploring different aspects of citizenship. Through the activities and discussion with each other we learnt about the government citizenship initiative, what it would mean for us and how we could make our voices heard. In actual fact, when the citizenship initiative comes into practice it will mean very little change for most young people because schools will simply re-label activities they are already teaching so as to incorporate all that they must within their already busy schedules.

Without meaning to be pious, I learnt an awful lot from the Your Turn course. Without running similar courses for every school-aged child in the country, I think that the interest and enthusiasm for citizenship, despite the government drive, will be minimal. Some of the experiences I had will stay with me for the rest of my life, it was utterly fantastic. We were given a guided tour around the Houses of Parliament, we sat in on a court in session, we were given a virtual million to invest on the stock market (my group managed to end up £23 million in debt after investing in Rail Track!), we learnt how to operate an X-ray machine, we debated with MPs, things that most 13-year-olds would never get to do. But without the chance to see the things we saw and talk to the people we talked to, there is no reason for citizenship to be anything new or exciting, and unless it is exciting the country's students will not sit up and take notice of it.

As Eleanor says, there is as yet no clear, shared meaning of 'citizenship'. Much of what she became involved in seems to have involved gaining an insight into education, the economy, health care, government, the criminal justice system, image and culture. Maybe these insights were an introduction to aspects of the adult world, particularly around 'political literacy', rather than explorations of how we as individuals collectively live in communities. Eleanor also shows some understandable scepticism about whether 'citizenship' indicates a more fundamental social or political change. She also makes the point that the young people involved were not representative of the young people in her school; for this kind of initiative to have real impact, young people from all backgrounds, including those most at risk of social exclusion, need to be equally involved. But this sort of programme has the potential to engage young people in an understanding of how things work and how they can be a part of things.

Behind any support for citizenship in schools can be some rather different ideas about children and young people. For some this will be a useful sort of apprenticeship, a matter of training children and young people to make a useful contribution later on in their lives. But for others, children and young people are already citizens and what they lack is the ability to act as such – to participate meaningfully. Whether the idea of citizenship is one that will catch the public imagination and form a constructive way of thinking about the individual and the community remains to be seen. However superficial or profound the use of the concept of citizenship turns out to be, it should further encourage schools to strengthen their interaction with their wider communities and, at the very least, it could encourage schools to develop some essential skills for children and young people – skills of listening, questioning and developing the vocabulary of discussion and debate.

Key points

- Moving beyond consultation to real participation is essential if community work is to be effective.

- Participation needs to be built into institutions' and agencies' values and become part of planning, delivery, resourcing and evaluation of service provision.

Conclusion

Now we have come to the end of this unit I hope you have been able to see how communities, and community work, for good or ill, can influence the quality of people's lives. We need communities that act as positive forces in our lives; many more of us should be living in places that can provide efficient and effective public services, within an inclusive community setting. For children and young people the influences of their communities may be particularly profound and long lasting, particularly where the risk of social exclusion arises. We have also looked closely at both 'top down' and 'bottom up' programmes and projects and at the nature of community work. You will, I hope, have gained some useful insights into how effective different approaches can be and how they relate to wider health and social policies.

Study skills: Choosing a course for next year

Around this time of the year you receive literature from the OU on choosing a course to follow K100. Are you ready to think so far ahead when you are not yet half way through K100? Well, you have several weeks before you need to return the form and you can change your mind for some time after that (the relevant dates are given in the literature) – but here are some first thoughts.

If you decide to take another OU course you can, in principle, choose virtually any on offer – from *Astronomy and Planetary Science* to *Homer: Poetry and Society*. However, if you are looking to build on what you are learning in K100, the obvious choices are the Level 2 courses in the School of Health and Social Welfare. Actually, you are free to go straight to a third-level course, but perhaps you should think about your marks for your K100 assignments and ask your tutor's advice before deciding to skip a level. Alternatively, you might prefer to stay at Level 1 for another year and take, say, the Social Sciences Faculty's Level 1 course. (At one time all OU students took two Level 1 courses.)

If you *are* choosing an SHSW Level 2 course, you probably ought to think a bit about whether you might want to complete a diploma and then eventually a degree – and whether you would want a general BA, or BSc degree, or a 'named degree', such as 'Health Studies', or 'Health and Social Care'. Or might you want to train as a social worker or a nurse? Some of these options will narrow down your choices, and you do not want to find out, some years from now, that you have excluded yourself from a qualification you would have liked to achieve. Make time to look through the literature to see what is involved in the various routes you might want to follow.

Beyond SHSW, there are courses relevant to the care field in the Faculties of Social Sciences and Science, the Open University Business School and in the School of Education. Alternatively, you might prefer to concentrate on vocational training, or to transfer your OU credits and continue your studies in another university.

If you would like advice in picking your way through all these options, phone the Student Advisory Service at your OU Regional Centre. Also, talk with fellow students, or with your tutor.

References

Barnardo's *Counting the Cost*, Advertising Campaign 2001/2002.

Clark, A. and Moss, P. (2001) *Listening to Young Children: The mosaic approach*, National Children's Bureau and Joseph Rowntree Foundation, National Children's Bureau, London.

Department for Education and Employment (1998) *Meeting the Childcare Challenge: A framework and consultation document*, The Stationery Office, London.

Department of Health, Department for Education and Employment and Home Office (2000) Appendix A 'The Assessment Framework', *Framework for the Assessment of Children in Need and Their Families*, The Stationery Office, London.

Department of Social Security (1999) *Opportunities for All. Tackling poverty and social exclusion*, The Stationery Office, London.

Eisenstadt, N. (2000) in *Upstart. The newsletter for everyone in Sure Start*. Summer 2000, DfEE Publications.

Fordham, G. and Lawless, P. (2002) *The Groundwork Movement: Its role in neighbourhood renewal*, Joseph Rowntree Foundation, York.

King's Fund (2001) *Healthy Neighbourhoods*, www.kingsfund.org.uk [accessed 31.7.02].

Land, H. (2002) *Facing the Future. Policy Papers, Meeting the Childcare Challenge*, Daycare Trust, London.

Malik, M. (2001) 'Children now', *The Membership Magazine of the National Children's Bureau*, National Children's Bureau, London.

Rose, W. and Aldgate, J. (2000) 'Knowledge underpinning the assessment framework', in Department of Health, *Assessing Children in Need and their Families: Practice guidance*, The Stationery Office, London.

Scottish Parliament (2000) *The Policy Framework for Tackling Poverty and Social Exclusion in Scotland*, www.scottish.parliament.uk [accessed 31.7.02].

Social Exclusion Unit (2001) *Preventing Social Exclusion*, www.open.gov.seu [accessed 2.1.02]

Social Exclusion Unit (2001) *Consultation Report on Young Runaways*, www.open.gov.seu [accessed 2.1.02]

Social Exclusion Unit (1999) *Bridging the Gap: New opportunities for 16–18-year-olds not in education, employment or training*, www.open.gov.seu [accessed 2.1.02]

Social Exclusion Unit (1998) *Rough Sleeping*, www.open.gov.seu [accessed 2.1.02]

Social Exclusion Unit (1999) *Teenage Pregnancy*, www.open.gov.seu [accessed 2.1.02]

Social Exclusion Unit (1998) *Truancy and School Exclusion*, www.open.gov.seu [accessed 2.1.02]

Social Exclusion Unit (2001) *A New Commitment to Neighbourhood Renewal. National Strategy Action Plan*, www.open.gov.seu [accessed 2.1.02].

Taylor, M. (2000) *Top-down Meets Bottom-up: Neighbourhood management*, Joseph Rowntree Foundation, York.

The Mental Health Foundation (1999) *Bright Futures: Promoting children and young people's mental health*, The Mental Health Foundation, London.

UNICEF (United Nations Children's Fund) (2000) *Innocenti Report Card No.1, A league table of child poverty in rich nations*, UNICEF, Florence, Italy.

United Nations Convention on the Rights of the Child (1999) Article 12 *Respect. A report into how well Article 12 of the UN Convention on the Rights of the Child is put into practice across the UK*, UNCRC.

Acknowledgements

Grateful acknowledgement is made to the following sources for permission to reproduce material in this book:

Illustrations

p. 116: John Birdsall Photography; *p. 124 (top left):* Peter Olive/ Photofusion; *p. 124 (top right):* www.shoutpictures.com; *p. 124 (bottom):* Diamond Theatre School; *p. 125:* John Walmsley Photography; *p. 126:* Mike Levers/Open University; *p. 127:* Bob Watkins/Photofusion; *p. 129:* Nick Cobbing; *pp. 134-137:* © Barnardo's.

Figures

Fig. 1: © Crown copyright material is reproduced with the permission of the Controller of HMSO and Queen's Printer for Scotland; *Fig. 2:* A League Table of Child Poverty in Rich Nations: Innocenti Report Card, UNICEF Innocenti Research Centre.

Unit 13

Finding Out about Services in the Community

Prepared for the course team by Martin Robb, updated by Andrew Northedge

While you are working on Unit 13, you will need:

- *The Good Study Guide*
- Skills video
- Care Systems and Structures
- Assignment Book

Contents

Introduction

Unit 13 focuses on:

- assessing individual needs

- finding out about services in the community

- enabling people to make use of services

- reviewing progress on study skills

- tackling examinations

- working with numbers.

In Block 3 we have been exploring the relationship between health and care services and the communities they serve. In this unit the focus is on developing your own skills in working in the community. It may be that you have a lot of experience of working in community settings, either as a paid worker or as a volunteer. Perhaps the kind of community-based health and care services described in Units 10–12 were familiar to you from your own experience. If this is the case, this unit will give you an opportunity to reflect on some of the skills that you have gained through this work and to gather evidence of them. Or it may be that you are involved in care work, but not in a community setting. If so, this unit may help you develop skills that will be useful in the future. Finally, you may not be directly involved in any form of care work, whether paid or unpaid. However, I hope that working through the activities in this unit will help to consolidate what you have learnt in Units 10–12, by giving you the chance to apply it to some practical examples.

Central themes of the unit

The particular skill that this unit focuses on is *finding out about services in the community.* In Unit 10 you encountered some of the difficulties in gaining access to services provided in the community. Part of the problem lies in finding out *what* services are available and *who* provides them. The aim of this unit is to help you develop skills in gathering information about services in the local community, and in matching services to a range of individual needs. As far as the principles of good practice go, the unit is particularly relevant to promoting and supporting people's rights to appropriate services.

This unit presents a series of linked activities. The activities make use of a number of short case studies which feature individuals with a range of needs. I want you to imagine that the individuals featured in the case studies live in *your own local area* and to find out about local services which meet their needs. I have tried to ensure that you will be able to carry out all the activities from your own home or study base. However, if you find you have difficulties carrying out some of the activities, please talk to your tutor about what to do.

Section 1
Assessing needs

To make the process of finding out about services and facilities as real as possible, I have chosen to concentrate on a few individual cases. The first few activities will introduce you to them, and involve you in making a brief assessment of the needs of the individuals featured.

Activity 1	**Assessing individual needs**

Allow about 30 minutes

There are three case studies below. They are fictitious but drawn from real life. I have tried to illustrate the range of needs and contexts which community-based workers may find themselves dealing with. Read through the examples now.

Case study 1

Mandy Brown is a 19-year-old white woman. She is a lone parent, living in a rented flat with a two-year-old son, Sean. She moved to the area quite recently with her partner Gary, who has since left her, and she doesn't know anyone locally. Mandy needs money to support herself and Sean. She has an interview for a part-time job at a factory a few miles away, but there is no workplace crèche and she doesn't know where she could leave Sean. She doesn't have a car and has to rely on buses and taxis. Mandy thinks she may be entitled to more welfare benefits than she's getting. An additional worry is that the flat is damp and Sean has bad asthma.

Case study 2

Mohammed and Zeinab Bhatti are in their seventies and live in their own house. Mr Bhatti ran a small business until forced to retire after a bad fall a few years ago. He is increasingly frail and dependent on his wife to help him around the house and to carry out household chores. However, Mrs Bhatti has arthritis and is beginning to find the role of full-time carer a difficult one. The Bhattis are Muslim; they came to Britain from Pakistan 20 years ago. They have two grown-up children – their son is working in Pakistan and their daughter has moved with her husband to another town and is unable to help on a regular basis. Mr Bhatti feels cut off from social contacts – he used to be active in the local Asian community and had a wide circle of friends. Mrs Bhatti would like some help looking after her husband and to have an occasional break from household chores.

> ### Case study 3
>
> Colin Grant is a 35-year-old African-Caribbean man, born and brought up in Britain. He has learning difficulties and lives at home with his parents. Mr Grant senior works as an electrician for the local council, while Mrs Grant has not had a job since Colin was born. When he was younger, Colin attended a special school and a number of day centres, but a change in Mr Grant senior's job has meant a house move to a new area. Colin's parents are in their early sixties and wonder how long they will be able to manage looking after him without help. Mrs Grant in particular finds looking after Colin full-time quite stressful, and her husband thinks she may be suffering from depression. Colin himself doesn't have any friends in the area and gets bored and restless at home all day with his mother. On the other hand, his parents would like him to carry on living at home for as long as possible.

Imagine that you have been asked to assess the *needs* of the people featured in these case studies, based on the information given here. Read each of the case studies carefully, then for each one note down your answers to these questions.

- What do the people in the case study identify as their main needs?
- What other needs do you think they may have?

Comment
To help you with this and the following activities, I will use case study 1 as an illustration. These are the notes I made.

Mandy and Sean Brown's needs include:

- affordable childcare for Sean, so Mandy can go out to work
- advice/help for Mandy with claiming welfare benefits
- advice/support in treating Sean's asthma
- help with moving to somewhere less damp.

In carrying out this first activity you have already begun to practise a number of skills. The first stage in helping someone gain access to services is to *assess* their individual needs. In this brief exercise, you have had to elicit, or draw out, from the information you have been given, the relevant information and to make *judgements* about individuals' needs.

In a real-life setting you would obviously have access to more information than you have been given here. You would be able to interview individuals directly and perhaps draw on information from other sources. In the next activity you are asked to think about what *further* information you would need to have if you were making an assessment of the individuals in these case studies 'for real'.

Activity 2
What else would I need to know?

Allow about 20 minutes
Go back over your notes on each of the case studies in Activity 1. For each case, make a brief note of what else you might need to know if you were asked to make a 'real' assessment of that person's needs.

Comment   Here is what I noted down for case study 1:

I thought that I would want to know more about Mandy's partner, Gary, and the circumstances in which he left. Is the child his, and is he financially liable for Sean's support? If so, is he sending Mandy any money? Is he likely to return, and will this cause any problems for Mandy? Given Sean's problems with asthma, I thought it would be useful to know more about his medical history, and perhaps about Mandy's own. Her education and employment history might also throw up information that would be useful in helping her in the future. In terms of housing, I wondered whether she had ever lived in, or applied for, local authority accommodation, and whether she thought she was eligible?

I hope you managed to come up with at least two or three instances of 'further information needed' for each of the case studies. There is always a balance to be struck between the costs involved in obtaining information about an individual's circumstances and the benefits that such information might offer. Part of the skill in assessing a person's needs lies in picking out from the details of their life the information which will help you to make a proper assessment of their needs.

Key point

- Assessing an individual's need for services involves paying close attention to the details of their circumstances.

Section 2
Sources of information

You should now have some sense of the *needs* of each of the individuals featured in the three case studies. The next stage is to think about how those needs might be met by health and social care services in the local community. But first, it will be useful to have a general sense of the *kinds* of services that might be of help to the individuals in the case studies.

Activity 3   **What kinds of services?**

Allow about 15 minutes   Having made a note of Mandy and Sean Brown's needs, I drew up a list of the kinds of services I thought they might need:

Needs	Kinds of services
Childcare	Nursery or childminder
Welfare benefits	Information/advice service
Sean's asthma	Asthma clinic or support group
Damp flat	Housing information/advice service

Look back over the notes that you made in Activity 1 on Mr and Mrs Bhatti's needs (case study 2). Then draw up your own chart matching *needs* to *kinds of services.* At this stage don't worry about trying to think of particular organisations or agencies, but think in more general terms. Then do the same for the Grant family (case study 3).

Comment   How did you get on with the other examples? Don't worry if you didn't know whether particular services existed, or who might provide them. The important thing is to have a general sense of what might help the individuals concerned. For example, for case study 2 your list may have included a need for meals-on-wheels or a home carer, and perhaps attendance at a day centre for older people for Mr Bhatti. For case study 3, you might have thought of a day centre for Colin, as well as respite care to give his parents a break.

The next stage is to get a clearer sense of which organisations and agencies provide these services. Once again I have made some notes for case study 1 to give you an idea of the kinds of organisations that provide services.

Case study 1

Childcare facilities, such as nurseries, crèches and childminders, are provided by a whole range of organisations – some private, some charitable or voluntary organisations, some local authority controlled. But most childcare provision is inspected and approved by the local authority's social services department, so I thought they would be a good, central source of information.

Welfare benefits are the responsibility of the Benefits Agency, which is a central government agency, but has offices in local areas where people can make enquiries and claims.

How do you begin to find out about services in the local community?

Health services, such as those that might provide assistance with Sean's asthma, are now mostly under the control of local NHS trusts, but primary health care (as you saw in Unit 10) tends to be provided through local GPs' surgeries or health centres.

Housing is the responsibility of local authorities in Britain and the Housing Executive in Northern Ireland.

You can see that this list includes:

- *statutory* providers, both national (such as the Benefits Agency) and local (the social services department, the NHS trust and the council's housing department)
- *voluntary* agencies
- *private* organisations.

(Earlier units in the course have made use of the term 'mixed economy of care' to refer to this diversity of kinds of providers.) Identifying the most appropriate service to meet an individual's needs will involve being aware of the range of providers in the locality.

Activity 4   Who provides the services?

Allow about 20 minutes   Who provides the kinds of services that you identified for case studies 2 and 3? For each of the services that you listed in Activity 3, try to write down the name of an organisation or agency that you think might provide this service.

    To help you with this activity, you may want to refer to Care Systems and Structures. I don't expect your notes to be as detailed as those I made for case study 1. And don't worry if you can't match a name to each of the services. You may have to make an intelligent guess at this stage – there will be a chance to check out your guess in a later activity.

Comment   How did you get on? It doesn't matter if you couldn't think of a service provider to match every kind of service you had identified. The important point to note here is the *range* of service providers that exists in any local area. For case study 2, you may have identified the local social services department as the first point of contact for information about a number of the services required by Mr and Mrs Bhatti, but you might also have thought of voluntary or charitable agencies that work with older people. For case study 3, social services would again be a key service provider, especially for respite care. Mrs Grant may need to see her GP about treatment for depression – but she may also get help from an informal support group for carers of people with learning difficulties.

Having considered the kinds of services that an individual might need, how do you go about gaining *information* about them?

Activity 5   Identifying sources of information

Allow about 15 minutes   For this activity, I want you to imagine that the individuals featured in the case studies live in your local area, close to where you yourself live. If you found yourself in the role of helping or supporting these individuals, where would you encourage them to begin to look for *information* about the services to meet their needs? Using the list you have built up of kinds of services and likely providers, make a list of possible *sources of information* that might help the individuals in each scenario. Try to think as widely as possible.

Below I have provided notes for case study 1, but try to make a list for *all three* case studies, before looking at my notes.

Comment   Case study 1

Thinking of the services that might help Mandy Brown, I came up with this list of possible sources of information for my own area:

- phone book /Yellow Pages
- Thomson Local directory
- websites on the internet
- local newspapers
- notices in doctor's surgery
- library
- cards in newsagent's window
- council offices
- Citizens Advice Bureau.

Was your list similar to this, or did you think of different places where you, or the people in the examples, could look for information? The kinds of sources you mentioned will vary, depending on the kinds of services needed and on the nature of the local community.

I hope your own examples helped you to see the *variety* of possible sources of information about health and social care services. Some of the sources you identified may be service providers themselves – such as the doctor's surgery or health centre. Others may be general information or advice points, such as the CAB or library, or even cards in the newsagent's window. Increasingly, computer technology is changing the ways in which information is provided: many local authorities, for example, display details of their services on the internet, which you can access either from your home or at a library and there are other sources of information in your own home such as local newspapers and phone directories. In the next section we will be focusing on the kinds of information that can be gained from these sources.

Key points

- Health and social care services are provided by a wide variety of statutory, voluntary and private organisations.

- It is important to be aware of the range of service providers in the local area when trying to find services to meet individual needs.

- Information about health and social care services can be gained from a wide variety of sources.

Section 3
Finding out about services

Having located some possible sources of information, we now need to explore how *useful* they are in helping us gain access to health and social care services. The next activity, which is rather longer than the others, will give you 'hands on' experience of using some of these information sources. Obviously, it would take more time than we have in this unit to search through *all* the sources of information you have identified in Activity 5. To limit the scale of the exercise, I want you to use only those sources of information that you have access to in your own home or study setting. This will probably mean restricting your list to the phone book, Yellow Pages, local directories or guides that you happen to have, recent local newspapers or, if you have a computer, the World Wide Web.

Activity 6 | **Finding out about services in your area**

Allow about 1 hour 30 minutes | For this activity you will need to take each of the case studies in turn. For each one, use the sources of information that you have to hand to find out as much as you can about the services that each individual might be able to make use of if they lived in your area.

To give you an idea of where to look and what to look for, here are the results of my own search for information relevant to case study 1. Read through my notes before going on.

Case study 1

Before giving details of how I got on, it is important to say that I based my answers on the area where I live, which is a medium-sized industrial town in the Midlands of England. The town has a borough council and is also part of a shire county, which means that some services are also provided by the county council. The local government structures, and the kinds of local agencies that exist in your area, will vary depending on which part of the United Kingdom you live in and on the kind of area you live in – for example, whether it is urban or rural.

I took each of Mandy and Sean Brown's needs for services in turn.

Childcare provision

I started with the Yellow Pages. Under 'nurseries, child' I was referred to the entries for 'crèche facilities and services' and 'day nurseries'. The nearest crèche facility mentioned was in a neighbouring large town – too far by public transport. 'Day nurseries' was more promising – there was a long list of these, although on closer inspection only two in the town itself. I then looked under 'childcare', which listed crèches and day nurseries, and also gave details of 'nanny and childcare agencies', including one close by, but I guessed this kind of service might be too expensive for Mandy.

The Thomson Local directory had a section headed 'childminders', but there were only three entries, none of them local; it didn't list nurseries at all.

Having found out that childcare was the responsibility of social services departments, which come under county councils (or their equivalent), I looked up the county council in the front 'business' section of the phone book. There I found a full-page display entry for social services, which included separate phone numbers, at County Hall, for 'services for children, families and older people' and 'services for under eights and childminders'. I also looked in the main entry for the social services department and found a more local entry – in my own town – for something called 'Family Support Teams' and even an 'Under 10s Team', which I thought might be worth following up.

 I then tried the internet. I dialled up and when the web-browser opened I selected my favourite search engine. I typed in 'childcare' and the name of my town, and found the first three 'results' were websites offering information about local day nurseries in my area. I then tried 'childcare' and the name of a nearby town and got a more mixed listing, though there was one very useful site called 'UpMyStreet' offering a whole range of local information, including about childcare of various kinds. There isn't space here to go into detail, but I quickly found a wide range of leads I could follow up.

Benefits advice

Browsing through the first few pages of the phone book, I came across a list of national numbers to ring for advice on benefits, including the Family Credit Helpline, which looked as though it might be of use to Mandy, even if it wasn't a local service.

I then looked up 'benefits' in the front section of the phone book and found a display entry for the Benefits Agency, which is part of the Department of Social Security. This entry gave details of the address and phone number of local offices by post codes. There was also more information here about helplines, including one for child benefit.

This page also referred me to a separate entry on 'child benefit,' which gave details both of the national Child Benefit Centre in Newcastle, 'for enquiries about child benefit, one parent benefit and guardian's allowance', and also the Child Support Agency.

I looked up 'advice' and 'information services' in the Yellow Pages: there was nothing in my own town, but the neighbouring town had a number of information centres, including one specifically for young people. I was also referred to the entry on 'social services and welfare organisations', which mentioned a number of support groups, although none particularly relevant to Mandy's needs. I then thought that a Citizens Advice Bureau would offer independent advice, so I looked them up in the phone book and found that there was one locally.

 When I tried the internet, I typed 'benefits' in the search engine and immediately found myself directed to the site of the government's Department for Work and Pensions which provided an A-Z directory of the benefits and services available and a page specifically about benefits and services for families and children, with links to the relevant services (http://www.dwp.gov.uk/lifeevent/benefits/index.htm, [accessed 1.6.02]). I also found several sites which dealt with benefit systems in other countries, so I realised I should have typed 'UK benefits' to narrow my search.

Asthma support

When I looked up 'health' in the phone book, I came across a number of national sources of information and advice, including a general Health Information Service. In the first few pages of the phone book I found a national asthma helpline. I thought that this might have been able to put Mandy in touch with more local forms of support. The 'health services' entry in the phone book listed all the local NHS trusts and referred to their entries elsewhere in the book. My own local NHS trust didn't have a specific entry for help with asthma (although it did for other conditions, such as diabetes and AIDS). However, it did give details of a community health clinic and a child development centre, where the local health visitors are based. I thought it more likely that Mandy's first approach should be to her local GP surgery or health centre: she would find out her nearest one by looking under 'doctors: medical practitioners' in the Yellow Pages.

On the internet I typed 'asthma' and the name of my town into the search engine and found many sites concerned with asthma in general, including the NHS Direct site (www.nhs.uk/ [accessed 1.6.02]), and also sites with information about local support for asthma sufferers.

Housing

I looked under 'housing' in the business section of the phone book, but this only gave details of providers of sheltered accommodation. But since I had an idea that housing was provided by local authorities, I looked up my local borough council, which had a full-page display entry. There was a list of numbers for the Housing and Environmental Health Department, including a general enquiries number, as well as numbers for home improvement grants and other needs, which may have been of use to someone in Mandy's position.

Using my internet search engine I typed 'UK housing' and immediately found several sites with useful information, including the government's Housing Corporation (www.housingcorp.gov.uk/ [accessed 1.6.02]), Housingnet (www.housingnet.co.uk/ [accessed 1.6.02]) and the Housing Resource Guide (www.housinguk.org/ [accessed 1.6.02]).

Now carry out your own search for information for all three case studies. Make brief notes of your findings. You will need to allow a fair amount of time for this activity and to divide it up equally between the three case studies. Searching for information can be a frustrating task. Don't worry if you draw a blank for a particular service – leave it and move on to the next one.

Comment How did you get on with this activity? If you live in a city or large town, you may have found a wider range of services than I did. I certainly discovered that my neighbouring larger town has a wider variety of provision – independent advice and information centres, for example – than my own area. On the other hand, if you live in a small town or village, you probably found it quite hard to find any services that were within easy reach of where you live.

My own experience of doing this activity left me with a number of thoughts. I found that it is quite difficult – unless you know exactly what you are looking for – to find out about health and social care services in your area, using the sources of information available to most people. My experience was often of trying several approaches – different 'key words', for example – before I hit on the right kind of information. Even then, it was easier to find out about services that were the responsibility of large, statutory bodies – such as county councils and NHS trusts – than about those provided by smaller voluntary or charitable organisations. For these, you really needed to know the name of an organisation, and what kind of service it provided, before you knew where to look. However, if you have access to the internet it can certainly help a lot in pointing you to relevant sources and in finding a pathway through all the possibilities to the ones particularly relevant to you. Increasingly the internet is becoming the obvious first port of call in looking for care related information. If you don't have access to a computer at home, or skills in using the internet, it is certainly worth making a trip to your local library and seeking support in learning how to search for websites with information relevant to you.

Was this your experience too, working on the other case studies? Were there services that you tried to find out about, using the information sources you had to hand, but were unable to? Once again, in a real-life situation, with more time available and the opportunity to search more widely, you would be able to make use of a greater variety of information sources. The next two activities will give you a chance to think about other sources of information that you might use – if you had more time and were able to get out and about in the local area.

Activity 7   **Using information sources in the local community**

Allow about 30 minutes

Scene 7 of the skills video is a dramatised version of case study 1, the story of Mandy and Sean Brown. In recording this scene, we have placed these characters in a fictional setting – the Manor Estate – and imagined that Mandy has to find out for herself about the services that may meet her needs.

As you watch the video scene, make a note of all the *sources of information* that Mandy uses to find out about local services. You may need to watch the scene two or even three times.

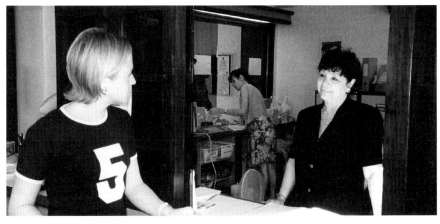

Mandy Brown calls in at the local health centre

Comment   Mandy calls in at the *community centre* on the estate, where she finds out about the local playgroup from Steve, the unemployed volunteer at the centre. Steve is also the means by which she finds out about the local health centre. The receptionist at the *health centre* provides Mandy with information about GP services, and it's also there that she picks up a leaflet about getting help with Sean's asthma. Later we see Mandy on the phone – we don't know exactly who she's talking to, but she's advised that she needs to contact the *benefits office*, and the local *council* about her housing needs. Finally, we see Mandy talking to an adviser at the local *Citizens Advice Bureau*.

Mandy made use of a number of different *kinds* of information sources available to her in the local area. They ranged from the very *informal* – dropping in and chatting to Steve at the community centre – to the quite *formal* – an interview with a professional adviser at the CAB. As well as *face-to-face* conversations, Mandy also found out about what was available by making *phone calls*, and by picking up *printed information* (such as the asthma leaflet). Although the video scene focuses on a specific example, it has given us some sense of the range of information sources available in any local area. The next activity will give you a chance to apply this to the examples you worked on earlier.

Activity 8   **Where else could you look?**

Allow about 15 minutes   Go back to the notes you made for Activity 7. Imagine that you had more time and were able to get out and about in your local area. What other sources of information could *you* make use of to help meet the needs identified in the three case studies?

Comment   In Activity 7 I found out about *some* of the childcare options in my local area, but not all of them. It was only when I rang one of the social services numbers in the phone book that they offered to send me a complete list of registered childminders and day nurseries in the area. The leaflet included some information about the approximate costs of different kinds of childcare – something else that Mandy would need to know. Perhaps if I had contacted the CAB in the town centre, they might have put me in touch with a specialist, independent source of advice about benefits. And I know from past experience that my local GP surgery runs a regular asthma clinic, and holds details of similar specialist services.

I hope you managed to think of similar possibilities for this and the other two case studies. This activity, together with the dramatised example in the video, should have broadened your understanding of the range of information sources about health and social care services available within local communities, and of the variety of ways you can make use of them.

Key points

- Finding out about health and social care services involves using a number of different sources of information and a range of different approaches.

- Information about services is usually available within the local community – sources of information may be informal or formal, and may involve face-to-face meetings, telephone contact or printed material.

Section 4
Reviewing your learning from experience

In this unit you have gained some experience in finding out about health and social care services in a particular local area, and attempting to relate these to the needs of individuals. In doing so, you have had a 'taste' of what it is like to be a potential service user or a care worker in the role of supporting a potential user, trying to gain access to information about service provision.

Before moving on to the final, study skills section of this unit, you will find it useful to *review* what you have learnt from your work on Sections 1–3.

Activity 9   **Skills review**

Allow about 15 minutes   Look back briefly over your notes on Activities 1–8. Make a quick list of the skills you think you have practised in doing these activities. (You may want to refer back to the idea of writing a reflective diary that was introduced in Unit 5 to help you structure your thoughts here.)

Comment   This was my list:

- assessing individual needs

- matching needs to appropriate services

- identifying sources of information

- using sources of information

- matching information about services to individual needs and circumstances.

You may have described the skills you thought you had practised in different ways. Whatever your answer, I hope you felt that, in carrying out this series of activities, you have been developing skills that are vital for community-based workers in health and social care.

As well as helping to develop your practice skills, your work on this part of the unit should have further increased your knowledge and understanding of the range of health and social care services, and the organisations and agencies that provide them. Your investigation of services in your own area will have given you a sense of the variety of providers in health and social care – not just national and local statutory agencies, but also a range of voluntary and private organisations, both formal and informal, large and small. Your work on the unit relates particularly to the fourth of the five principles of good practice, 'promote and support people's rights to appropriate services'.

4.1 Portfolio record

If you are keeping a portfolio record of your work on K100, you will want to add to it your notes from some of the activities in this unit.

In particular, it will be useful to include:

Activity 1 – checklist of needs and circumstances for the three case studies

Activity 3 – list matching needs to services

Activity 4 – list of service providers

Activity 5 – sources of information

Activity 6 – detailed notes on services in your own area

Activity 9 – list of skills.

Key point

- The process of finding out about local services and matching services to individual needs involves a range of skills that are vital for workers in health and social care.

Section 5
Study skills

5.1 Progress with your study skills at the half-way point

You are nearly at the half-way point of K100, so it's a good time to review your progress in developing skills as a student. Naturally, this is something only *you* can do, but the activities below will help.

Activity 10   **Have your skills changed?**

Allow about 5 minutes   Think first about how you would rate your skills at the time you started K100. Work down the left half of the table circling a score against each area of study skill. Then do the same down the right half of the table. Finally, for each skill area, subtract your score on the left from your score on the right and write the difference in the 'change' column on the right.

	At the start of K100					Now					Change
	very capable	*fairly capable*	*so-so*	*rather weak*	*very weak*	*very capable*	*fairly capable*	*so-so*	*rather weak*	*very weak*	
Reading	5	4	3	2	1	5	4	3	2	1	
Note taking	5	4	3	2	1	5	4	3	2	1	
Cassette study	5	4	3	2	1	5	4	3	2	1	
Tables and charts	5	4	3	2	1	5	4	3	2	1	
Study in groups	5	4	3	2	1	5	4	3	2	1	
Time management	5	4	3	2	1	5	4	3	2	1	
Keeping up morale	5	4	3	2	1	5	4	3	2	1	
Essay writing	5	4	3	2	1	5	4	3	2	1	

Comment   The 'change' column should now show those aspects of study where you think you have made most progress since February. Are there some areas where you have rated yourself two or more points better? In nearly three months that would be pretty good going. Even one point is a useful gain to have made. But what about the areas where you feel there is no gain? Should you be giving these more attention? I hope there aren't aspects of studying where your score is lower now than at the start. If there are, perhaps you should talk to your tutor about it.

Of course, if your ratings of your skills at the start of the course (left side of the table) are high then you had little room for improvement anyway and perhaps the study skills component of the course is not so important for you.

The columns headed 'Now' show where you think you still have work to do to strengthen your study skills.

Activity 11   **Analysing your scores**

Allow about 15 minutes

(a)   If you have some low scores in the 'Now' column get a sheet of paper and write those skill areas as headings down the side. Against each heading write a few ideas about how you could strengthen that skill area – such as experimenting with new approaches, talking to fellow students, asking your tutor, setting aside time to practise, or working with *The Good Study Guide.*

(b)   On a five-point scale give yourself a rating for 'confidence' as an OU student at the start of the course. Then rate your confidence now.

(c)   If you join up the numbers you ringed in the left half of the table (from row 1 to row 2, row 3 and so on) you will have a 'profile' of your view of yourself as a student at the start of K100. Get your study diary and scan back over the entries for the early weeks to see whether they match this profile.

Then join up the numbers to give your profile of skills as you see them now. Do your more recent diary entries match this profile?

(d)   If there are discrepancies between your diary and the profiles, how would you account for them?

Comment

(a)   Keep this sheet of notes in your study diary and look back at it from time to time to remind yourself (i) to keep working on these skills and (ii) of your plans for doing it.

(b)   Has your rating of your confidence increased since the start of the course? It could be that it has gone down because you were over-confident at the start, not realising what demands the course would make of you. Yet, now that you have coped with nearly half the course, you have every reason to be feeling more confident than in the early weeks. Many OU students say the growing self-confidence they experience as they confirm that they *can* study effectively at degree level is one of the greatest benefits of taking a course.

(c)   Did you find your 'profiles' interesting? They are not based on a proper 'test', of course – they simply tell you what you already thought. But you may not have thought so systematically before about where your strengths and weaknesses lie, and how they are changing as you study. The profiles are just a way of getting your ideas about yourself out into the open, on paper where you can look at them and perhaps rethink them.

(d)   Checking your profiles against your study diary is one way of re-examining your assumptions about yourself. You see yourself from a different angle doing these very different exercises. So which is the better view? Did you focus too much on your worries in your diary and forget your strengths? Are the profiles too crude to capture the variety of your capabilities? Perhaps you now have some new ideas about what to put in your diary.

Study skills: Being an insightful self-manager

As an independent student you have to be 'manager' of your studies and of yourself. In the study skills component of K100 we stress the importance of *reflecting* on yourself and your ways of working, so that you can think *strategically* about your studies – taking account of your personal aims and capabilities, instead of just ploughing ahead, following instructions and hoping for the best. Exercises like the diary and the self-rating profile are ways of trying to 'take yourself by surprise' – sneaking a look behind the established assumptions about yourself on which you base your daily life. They are meant to stimulate habits of self-reflection and self-analysis, and enable you to be a flexible and effective self-manager. This links to Kolb's reflective learning cycle in Section 1.6 of Chapter 1 of *The Good Study Guide* (p.20).

Study diary

You should have some interesting thoughts to put in your study diary this week after your work with these profiles.

5.2 The K100 examination

Having looked back to the start of the course, we now take a brief glance ahead to the end. You don't need to let the exam influence your experience of the course just yet. There's plenty of time later on. However, it's not a good idea to ignore the exam until the very last minute. As always, it pays to approach a study challenge with a *strategy*. So between now and the exam we shall periodically discuss aspects of exam and revision technique to support you in developing a strategy. We start with a general overview.

The nature of the exam

The first thing to say about the exam is that it is designed to enable you to do well. The course team does not believe in 'trick questions'. We want you to have every opportunity to use the knowledge and the writing skills you are developing throughout the course. Our ideal is that your exam result should be very similar to your assignment marks. If you are doing a reasonable proportion of the course reading and sending in your assignments then you are already preparing yourself well for the exam. Yet it is important not to be taken by surprise, so you need to familiarise yourself with what lies ahead.

Activity 12 | **The guidance in the Assignment Book**

Allow about 5 minutes

To get a quick idea of the main elements of preparing for and taking the exam, read Section 9 in the Assignment Book.

Comment

As you see, the recommended source of further advice is *The Good Study Guide*. But you don't need to look at it yet (unless you are keen to). You will be working on it a bit at a time in future skills units.

The exam is designed to allow you some choice in selecting what to revise. The specimen exam paper will show you what to expect and guide you in working out how to revise. It is also an excellent tool for helping you to practise answering questions and to develop a technique for the exam itself. We shall be coming to all these things in good time. For now the main message is that the exam is not something to worry about. If you approach it calmly, realistically and strategically, backed up by advice in the course materials and from your tutor, you have every reason to expect to do well.

Special circumstances

If you have a particular reason for anticipating difficulty with the exam, whether because of disability or not being able to attend an exam centre, contact either your tutor or the Regional Enquiry and Advisory Service at your Regional Centre. Special arrangements can usually be made where circumstances require them. But they need to be set up well in advance, so enquire in good time.

5.3 Working with numbers

Now we turn again to table-reading skills. Unit 11 questioned how well the care services meet the needs of different Minority Ethnic groups. And in Unit 10 you saw the importance, within the UK care services, of access to a GP. Clearly, the access that members of Minority Ethnic groups have to a GP is an important issue to explore. To investigate this we can turn to a survey carried out for the Health Education Authority and the NHS Ethnic Health Unit by the polling organisation MORI's Health Research Unit. The foreword to the 1994 report, *Black and Minority Ethnic Groups in England*, describes it as 'the most important and comprehensive study of knowledge, attitude, behaviour and health status among Black and Minority Ethnic groups in England' (Rudat, 1994, p. vii). Although the main report focuses on England, it also draws on a previous UK-wide survey (Health Education Authority, 1994). The figures I shall quote combine data from both surveys.

The report devotes a whole chapter to the challenges of constructing a sample to give an accurate picture for men and women of different age groups, within different ethnic groups, living in different parts of the country. The sample on which the findings are based was made up as follows:

African-Caribbean	708
Indian	1,017
Pakistani	927
Bangladeshi	665
Total	*3,317*

The report points out that:

> The ... sample sizes for each of the ethnic community groups allow for meaningful comparisons both between the groups, and with known UK figures. Some of the individual sub-groups (especially Pakistani and Bangladeshi women aged 50 to 74 years) have very small bases. As a result some of the comparisons in this report will need to be treated with some caution.

> (Rudat, 1994, p. 22)

The survey found that, as with the general UK population, a very high proportion of members of Black and Minority Ethnic groups are registered with a GP (98 per cent of African-Caribbean and 100 per cent of Indian, Pakistani and Bangladeshi, as compared with 99 per cent in the population as a whole). It explores a number of aspects of access to GPs. For example it reports that:

In the UK-wide survey 5% of the population describe physical access to their surgery as difficult ... The proportions who describe access as difficult are significantly higher amongst South Asians, particularly Bangladeshis (17% describe access as difficult).

(Rudat, 1994, p. 60)

One of the tables shows that within the population as a whole about *half* of those who had access difficulties reported that their surgery was too far away. However *three-quarters* of Bangladeshis gave this as the reason. Also within the population as a whole a *quarter* gave poor public transport as the reason access was difficult, but 40 per cent of African-Caribbeans gave this reason (Rudat, 1994, p. 61).

The table we are going to examine looks at surgery waiting times reported by members of different groups.

Table 1 Average waiting time before seeing doctor (minutes)

Age groups	All	Women			Men		
		16–29	30–49	50–74	16–29	30–49	50–74
UK population	18	20	17	15	19	18	17
African-Caribbean	27	28	32	26	20	24	26
Indian	30	29	28	46	22	31	26
Pakistani	33	32	30	41	36	34	33
Bangladeshi	50	49	52	49	49	46	52

Base: All those who saw doctor at last visit
(Rudat, 1994, Table 36, p. 63)

Activity 13 **Getting the broad picture**

Allow about 15 minutes

People were asked how long they had to wait before they saw the doctor at their last visit. Table 1 shows what they reported.

(a) How long on average do people remember having had to wait to see their GP?

(b) In general, is age an important factor in how long people have to wait?

(c) In general, is ethnic group an important factor in how long people have to wait?

Comment (a) On average people wait for 18 minutes (you look at the figure for the UK population as a whole, and for all age groups).

(b) The answer is no. You need to look along the row of figures for the UK population and see how much variation there is from the average figure of 18 minutes. All the figures are within two or three minutes off 18. Women and men in the younger groups report a little over 18 minutes – and women and men in the older groups report a little under 18 minutes, so perhaps there is a slight tendency for waits to be shorter for older people. Or perhaps it's to do with the way younger and older people remember and report their waits. (These are not *actual* waiting times, but what people remembered when they were asked by an interviewer.)

(c) Here the answer is very clearly yes. You should be reading down the column of figures below 'All'.

Activity 14   **Getting into the details**

Allow about 15 minutes   Let's explore these differences in waiting experiences of ethnic groups.

(a) Write a sentence roughly summarising the figures in the 'All' column.

(b) Is age a factor in the waiting times experienced within the different ethnic groups? (Tip: the figure at the left of each row is the average for that ethnic group. Scan along the row and where you see a figure which is more than three minutes above or below, write a small +5 or −7 against it. Then you will easily see where the main variations are.)

(c) Looking across the table as a whole are there any age or gender groups within the Minority Ethnic groups who experience roughly the same waiting times as the general population?

(d) Are there any age or gender groups who experience particularly long waiting times compared with the rest of their ethnic group?

Comment   (a) Here is my sentence: Although the average waiting time for the population as a whole is under 20 minutes, for African-Caribbeans, Indians and Pakistanis it is around half an hour and for Bangladeshis it is over three-quarters of an hour.

(b) This is quite a tricky question to answer. You need to look along the row for each ethnic group and compare against the figure under the 'All' column. The variations are not very great for Bangladeshis, but for the other ethnic groups there are one or two sub-groups which seem to stand out. However, there are no very obvious overall patterns.

(c) Young African-Caribbean and Indian men experience waiting times of around 20 minutes, which is roughly the same as the general population.

(d) Older Indian women experience waiting times a quarter of an hour longer than the average for Indians (46 minutes as compared with 30). Older Pakistani women wait eight minutes longer than the average for Pakistanis. Although older Bangladeshi women wait longer than either of these groups, it is an average wait within the Bangladeshi group. (We should remember here the caution about the relatively small sample sizes of these particular groups. However, differences as large as 8 or 15 minutes are not very likely to be just sampling errors.)

Figures like these raise lots of questions about why there should be such differences in reported waiting times and it would take a long discussion to work our way through all the possible reasons. The report itself says:

> *Previous surveys have shown that patients from black and minority ethnic communities are significantly more likely to attend open GP surgeries (surgeries which do not operate an appointment system) than comparative white groups ... The current survey supports these findings ... Whilst 79% of the UK population attend appointment-based surgeries, this falls to two-thirds of African-Caribbeans, and just over half of South Asians.*

> *(Rudat, 1994, p. 61)*

But the report also concludes that the differences in waiting times 'are too large to be accounted for by this factor alone' (Rudat, 1994, p. 62). Other possible factors include the extent to which different ethnic groups attend surgeries with a group practice or a single GP. However, neither of these factors seems helpful in explaining why older women in some ethnic groups should wait longer.

Exploring questions like these fully is a specialised field of enquiry and not one we can usefully dabble in here. However, we can draw the general conclusion that members of Black and Minority Ethnic groups experience significantly longer than average waiting times when they visit their GPs.

Study skills: Scanning data for trends

The skill you have been practising is: (a) finding your way into a table and then (b) scanning it for blips and trends. Look at the box headed 'Blips' on page 203 of *The Good Study Guide*.

1   The important first step was to recognise that the figure '18' at the top left was the UK average. All the other figures were deviations from this average.

2   The second step was to scan across from the 18 and down from it (the top row and the left-hand column). This quickly showed that variations along the row were small, while variations down the column were big. So age was not a major factor but ethnic group was.

3   You found that scanning down the columns for the different age groups was not very easy or productive because the differences are so big and uneven. But scanning along the rows showed you how much variation there was from the average for each ethnic group. Marking the main deviations on to the table quickly showed you that older Indian women were the group which deviated most sharply from the average for their group, and highlighted six other groups which deviated, though to a lesser extent, from their ethnic group average.

5.4 Developing your writing skills

We have talked about getting the material together for an essay, but how do you actually put the words on to paper?

Study skills: Word processing

Do you write your essays by hand, or use a computer word processor? You can be successful with K100 either way. But certainly there are many benefits in using a computer as a study tool – and word processing is perhaps the greatest. It is not simply the look of the documents you produce, but the ease with which you can draft and redraft. However, you need to be able to type, or have the time to learn. And obviously there is the matter of what you can afford (with your OU fees to pay as well) and of how much use you would expect to make of a computer beyond K100. If you have reached this stage of the course writing by hand, you may well feel it not worth worrying about any new challenges until the course is over. (After all, you will be hand-writing your exam anyway.) But just to give yourself food for thought if you don't have a computer – or to consider uses beyond word processing if you do have one – read Section 3.3 of Chapter 3 of *The Good Study Guide* (pp.57-63).

Getting the most from your computer

If you are using your computer a lot for your K100 studies you might like to read about organising your computer filing system in Section 3.4 of Chapter 3 of *The Good Study Guide* (pp.63-66).

Finally, we continue the theme of developing your writing skills.

Study skills: What is a good essay?

In Unit 5 you read Sections 10.1 and 10.3 of Chapter 10 of *The Good Study Guide*, and saw some examples of short essays written by new students. The essays were taken apart and discussed in detail to see the good ideas they contained – but also ways they could have been improved so as to make the ideas easier for readers to get hold of. Section 3 of Chapter 5 draws together some general principles from that analysis of the essays. It provides a basic guide to what you should be aiming for in your essays. Read the rest of Chapter 10 now (pp.262-295). You may need to remind yourself of the essays by glancing back over Section 2.

End of block assignment

All that remains now is TMA 03 (you may already have started it). See how far you can apply the principles you have been reading about in *The Good Study Guide*.

Section 6
Linking K100 studies to professional training

Healthcare connections

Access to care within the community

Unit 10 outlines four functions of primary care, the first being that GPs act as gatekeepers to other care services. Factors affecting access to care include geography, resources and the attitudes of care providers. People's own strategies in accessing healthcare also play a part, as Baldock and Ungerson's chapter shows.

Healthcare workers based in the community play an essential role in promoting access to and providing services commissioned by Primary Care Trusts. They need strategies to support people in overcoming barriers to access. Offprint 5 provides an example of how users can be informed of their eligibility for continuing healthcare.

Diversity within the community

Unit 11 shows the importance of sensitivity on the part of healthcare workers to the diverse cultures of patients and clients if they are to promote access to services. Reader Chapter 21 describes the effects of unconscious stereotyping by professionals and Section 3 shows how healthcare workers' use of power can affect the lives of patients and clients. Healthcare workers need to be aware of the effects of institutional racism and be able to identify discrimination and racism at all levels, whether individual, cultural or institutional. They also need strategies for challenging and changing attitudes to enable the provision of quality services to all members of the community.

Healthy communities

To promote healthy communities and prevent social exclusion, healthcare workers are encouraged to work across traditional boundaries and engage with other professionals.

Prevention is an important issue in healthcare. Unit 12, Section 2 provides an example of this with the Sure Start Programme for young children, where health visitors and other healthcare professionals work with families as part of a local multi-professional team.

Healthcare workers are also increasingly involved in working directly with people in the community, facilitating the setting up of community groups to promote health in the community.

Searching for care-related information in the community

Unit 13 introduces skills in assessing care needs and then locating relevant information about care services within the local community. Healthcare workers need to know how to find this information and also how to disseminate it in ways that all users will be able to access.

Social work connections

Accessing services

Unit 10 explains that within a 'primary care' model of service delivery the GP is the entry point for a wide range of welfare services. However the case of Jim and Marianne shows how barriers can be placed across this access route by geography, resource concerns or discriminatory attitudes. The same barriers can affect people's access to social work services through community care, though where someone fails to obtain services, social workers may become involved later on when the situation reaches crisis point.

The limits of care in the community

Social workers are asked to assess people in their social context and to consider the linkages within their communities. This can be a very positive process and can involve mobilising networks of support. However communities can also be hostile places. Some groups may face discrimination, making the community a source of stress as well as support.

Social exclusion

There is growing awareness that whole communities can be disadvantaged, so that individuals within them may be denied access, not only to welfare services, but a whole range of work and leisure opportunities which contribute to quality of life. This is known as social exclusion and it affects the majority of people social workers are involved with. Unit 12 looks at different levels of impact of child poverty upon the lives of young families such as Michelle and Bailey's.

Impact of racism

Another dimension of social exclusion is the way racism can shape service users' lives. Unit 11 explores contested ideas of 'race' and shows how the language of both racism and anti-racism is constantly evolving. The experiences of Lorna Campbell and the Asian families studied by Robina Shah show that racism is more than a set of offensive ideas. It involves power relations that can impact on every aspect of people's lives. Moreover, services themselves can reinforce and amplify discrimination, for example through stereotypes that Asian families prefer to 'look after their own'.

Institutional racism

Challenging racism entails much more than dealing with individual discrimination or harassment, important as that is. Social workers must consider racism in crucial areas such as education, the health service or housing. Institutional racism also exists within social care agencies themselves. For example, Black children are overrepresented in the Looked After System, as are Black adults in the coercive end of the mental health system. Also, social workers from Black and Minority Ethnic groups themselves face discrimination and are underrepresented at senior levels in their agencies.

Power of professionals

Social workers have considerable power over peoples' lives. This can be overt, as with the statutory powers given by such legislation as the *Children Act 1989* or the *Mental Health Act 1983*.

But power also works at the level of access to resources and information. Social workers must use this power ethically.

Anti-discriminatory practice

Unit 11 contains excellent examples, such as Moyenda and Dostiyo, of initiatives from within communities to develop services that meet the needs of marginalised groups. However, *all* social workers have a responsibility to work within anti-discriminatory and anti-oppressive frameworks. It is important that they understand policies and that they address racism and other forms of discrimination at an individual level.

Children and young people connections

Stereotyping, discrimination and institutional racism

Unit 11 reveals the impact stereotyped perceptions and thinking can have on Black and Minority Ethnic parents' access to services for their children (Reader Chapter 21), and then goes on to examine disadvantage and discrimination (direct or indirect) in services for Black and Minority Ethnic children and young people – showing how repeated and systematic discrimination amounts to institutional racism. All this is starkly illustrated by the case of Lorna Campbell. The unit discusses the overrepresentation of Black children in the care system and what this means both for those who provide services and for the children and young people themselves; there being growing concern about the impact that time spent in the care system has on the education and health of children and young people and their potential social exclusion.

Unit 11 also discusses positive approaches to working with diverse communities, including identifying discriminatory practices and taking action. Recent legislation and policy initiatives relevant to its discussions include Quality Protects (Children First in Wales) and the Children Leaving Care Act 2001.

Poverty and social exclusion

The impact of poverty and social exclusion on children and young people is discussed in Unit 12. The unit goes on look at how communities can improve the quality of life of children and young people. It draws attention to the emotional, physical, social and intellectual needs of children and young people and urgency of developing a range of services to meet these needs; as is being attempted both through national projects such as Sure Start and through local community-based action.

Listening and enabling

Unit 12 stresses the importance of listening to children and young people and enabling their participation. It explores the implications of The United Nations Convention on the Rights of the Child and the introduction of 'citizenship' into the National Curriculum, within a wider discussion of services and policies which involve and empower children and young people.

Assessing needs and finding out about services

Through the case of Mandy and Sean, Unit 13 gives you practice in assessing the needs of a mother and son, and finding out about services relevant to those needs within the complex mix of statutory, voluntary and private agencies working in this field.

References

Health Education Authority (1994) *Health and Lifestyles Surveys*, Health Education Authority, London.

Rudat, K. (1994) *Black and Minority Ethnic Groups in England*, Health Education Authority, London.

Acknowledgements

Grateful acknowledgement is made to the following sources for permission to reproduce material in this unit:

Text

pp. 174, 175, 176: Rudat, K. (1994) *Black and Minority Ethnic Groups in England*, reproduced with permission of the Health Education Authority.

Illustration

p.160: Crispin Hughes/Photofusion.

Table

Table 1: Rudat, K. (1994) *Black and Minority Ethnic Groups in England*, reproduced with permission of the Health Education Authority.